CATALYST

the prentice hall custom laboratory program for chemistry

Dr. Maria Valentino
Basic Chemistry
CHEM 121
Wright College
Physical Science

Pearson Learning Solutions

New York   Boston   San Francisco
London   Toronto   Sydney   Tokyo   Singapore   Madrid
Mexico City   Munich   Paris   Cape Town   Hong Kong   Montreal

Senior Vice President, Editorial and Marketing: Patrick F. Boles
Executive Marketing Manager: Nathan L. Wilbur
Sponsoring Editor: Debbie Coniglio
Operations Manager: Eric M. Kenney
Development Editor: Christina Martin
Production Manager: Jennifer Berry
Art Director: Renée Sartell
Cover Designer: Kristen Kiley

Cover Art: Courtesy of Photodisc, Age Fotostock America, Inc. and Photo Researchers.

Pyrex, pHydrion, Chem3D Plus, Apple, Macintosh, Chemdraw, Hypercard, graphTool, Corning, Teflon, Mel-Temp, Rotaflow, Tygon, Spec20, and LambdaII UV/Vis are registered trademarks.

Chem3D Plus is a registered trademark of the Cambridge Soft Corp.

The information, illustration, and/or software contained in this book, and regarding the above mentioned programs, are provided "as is," without warranty of any kind, express or implied, including without limitation any warranty concerning the accuracy, adequacy, or completeness of such information. Neither the publisher, the authors, nor the copyright holders shall be responsible for any claims attributable to errors, omissions, or other inaccuracies contained in this book. Nor shall they be liable for direct, indirect, special, incidental, or consequential damages arising out of the use of such information or material.

The authors and publisher believe that the lab experiments described in this publication, when conducted in conformity with the safety precautions described herein and according to the school's laboratory safety procedures, are reasonably safe for the students for whom this manual is directed. Nonetheless, many of the described experiments are accompanied by some degree of risk, including human error, the failure or misuse of laboratory or electrical equipment, mismeasurement, spills of chemicals, and exposure to sharp objects, heat, body fluids, blood or other biologics. The authors and publisher disclaim any liability arising from such risks in connections with any of the experiments contained in this manual. If students have questions or problems with materials, procedures, or instructions on any experiment, they should always ask their instructor for help before proceeding.

This special edition published in cooperation with Pearson Learning Solutions.

Printed in the United States of America.

Please visit our web site at *www.pearson custom .com*.

Attention bookstores: For permission to return any unsold stock, contact us at *pe-uscustomreturns@pearson.com*.

Pearson Learning Solutions, 501 Boylston Street, Suite 900, Boston, MA 02116
A Pearson Education Company
www.pearsoned.com

1 2 3 4 5 6 7 8 9 10 XXXX 14 13 12 11 10 09

ISBN 10: 0-536-66108-1
ISBN 13: 978-0-536-66108-1

Laboratory Safety: General Guidelines

1. Notify your instructor immediately if you are pregnant, color blind, allergic to any insects or chemicals, taking immunosuppressive drugs, or have any other medical condition (such as diabetes, immunologic defect) that may require special precautionary measures in the laboratory.

2. Upon entering the laboratory, place all books, coats, purses, backpacks, etc. in designated areas, not on the bench tops.

3. Locate and, when appropriate, learn to use exits, fire extinguisher, fire blanket, chemical shower, eyewash, first aid kit, broken glass container, and cleanup materials for spills.

4. In case of fire, evacuate the room and assemble outside the building.

5. Do not eat, drink, smoke, or apply cosmetics in the laboratory.

6. Confine long hair, loose clothing, and dangling jewelry.

7. Wear shoes at all times in the laboratory.

8. Cover any cuts or scrapes with a sterile, waterproof bandage before attending lab.

9. Wear eye protection when working with chemicals.

10. Never pipet by mouth. Use mechanical pipeting devices.

11. Wash skin immediately and thoroughly if contaminated by chemicals or microorganisms.

12. Do not perform unauthorized experiments.

13. Do not use equipment without instruction.

14. Report *all* spills and accidents to your instructor immediately.

15. Never leave heat sources unattended.

16. When using hot plates, note that there is no visible sign that they are hot (such as a red glow). Always assume that hot plates are hot.

17. Use an appropriate apparatus when handling hot glassware.

18. Keep chemicals away from direct heat or sunlight.

19. Keep containers of alcohol, acetone, and other flammable liquids away from flames.

20. Do not allow any liquid to come into contact with electrical cords. Handle electrical connectors with dry hands. Do not attempt to disconnect electrical equipment that crackles, snaps, or smokes.

21. Upon completion of laboratory exercises, place all materials in the disposal areas designated by your instructor.

22. Do not pick up broken glassware with your hands. Use a broom and dustpan and discard the glass in designated glass waste containers; never discard with paper waste.

23. Wear disposable gloves when working with blood, other body fluids, or mucous membranes. Change gloves after possible contamination and wash hands immediately after gloves are removed.

24. The disposal symbol indicates that items that may have come in contact with body fluids should be placed in your lab's designated container. It also refers to liquid wastes that should not be poured down the drain into the sewage system.

25. Leave the laboratory clean and organized for the next student.

26. Wash your hands with liquid or powdered soap prior to leaving the laboratory.

27. The biohazard symbol indicates procedures that may pose health concerns.

The caution symbol points out instruments, substances, and procedures that require special attention to safety. These symbols appear throughout this manual.

Measurement Conversions

Metric to American Standard	American Standard to Metric
Length	
1 mm = 0.039 inches	1 inch = 2.54 cm
1 cm = 0.394 inches	1 foot = 0.305 m
1 m = 3.28 feet	1 yard = 0.914 m
1 m = 1.09 yards	1 mile = 1.61 km
Volume	
1 mL = 0.0338 fluid ounces	1 fluid ounce = 29.6 mL
1 L = 4.23 cups	1 cup = 237 mL
1 L = 2.11 pints	1 pint = 0.474 L
1 L = 1.06 quarts	1 quart = 0.947 L
1 L = 0.264 gallons	1 gallon = 3.79 L
Mass	
1 mg = 0.0000353 ounces	1 ounce = 28.3 g
1 g = 0.0353 ounces	1 pound = 0.454 kg
1 kg = 2.21 pounds	

Temperature

To convert temperature:

$$°C = \frac{5}{9}(F - 32) \qquad °F = \frac{9}{5}C + 32$$

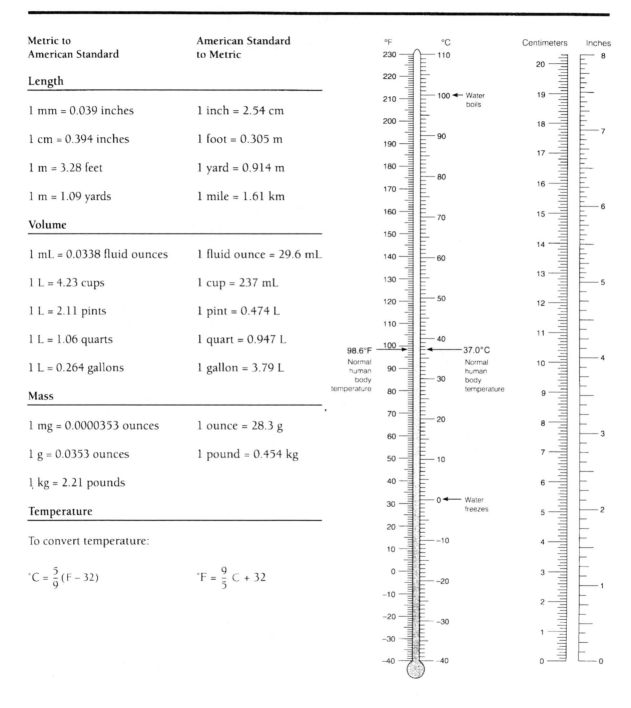

Contents

Periodic Table of the Elements with Element Names

KEY

6	Atomic number
C	Symbol
12.011	Atomic weight*
Carbon	Name

Atomic number	Symbol	Atomic weight*	Name
1	H	1.0080	Hydrogen
2	He	4.003	Helium
3	Li	6.941	Lithium
4	Be	9.013	Beryllium
5	B	10.81	Boron
6	C	12.011	Carbon
7	N	14.007	Nitrogen
8	O	15.999	Oxygen
9	F	18.998	Fluorine
10	Ne	20.179	Neon
11	Na	22.990	Sodium
12	Mg	24.305	Magnesium
13	Al	26.98	Aluminum
14	Si	28.09	Silicon
15	P	30.974	Phosphorus
16	S	32.066	Sulfur
17	Cl	35.453	Chlorine
18	Ar	39.948	Argon
19	K	39.098	Potassium
20	Ca	40.08	Calcium
21	Sc	44.96	Scandium
22	Ti	47.90	Titanium
23	V	50.94	Vanadium
24	Cr	51.996	Chromium
25	Mn	54.94	Manganese
26	Fe	55.85	Iron
27	Co	58.94	Cobalt
28	Ni	58.71	Nickel
29	Cu	63.55	Copper
30	Zn	65.38	Zinc
31	Ga	69.72	Gallium
32	Ge	72.60	Germanium
33	As	74.92	Arsenic
34	Se	78.96	Selenium
35	Br	79.904	Bromine
36	Kr	83.80	Krypton
37	Rb	85.468	Rubidium
38	Sr	87.62	Strontium
39	Y	88.906	Yttrium
40	Zr	91.22	Zirconium
41	Nb	92.91	Niobium
42	Mo	95.94	Molybdenum
43	Tc	(98)	Technetium
44	Ru	101.1	Ruthenium
45	Rh	102.91	Rhodium
46	Pd	106.4	Palladium
47	Ag	107.868	Silver
48	Cd	112.41	Cadmium
49	In	114.82	Indium
50	Sn	118.70	Tin
51	Sb	121.75	Antimony
52	Te	127.60	Tellurium
53	I	126.905	Iodine
54	Xe	131.30	Xenon
55	Cs	132.91	Cesium
56	Ba	137.33	Barium
(57-71)			
72	Hf	178.50	Hafnium
73	Ta	180.95	Tantalum
74	W	183.85	Wolfram
75	Re	186.21	Rhenium
76	Os	190.2	Osmium
77	Ir	192.2	Iridium
78	Pt	195.09	Platinum
79	Au	197.0	Gold
80	Hg	200.59	Mercury
81	Tl	204.37	Thallium
82	Pb	207.21	Lead
83	Bi	208.98	Bismuth
84	Po	(209)	Polonium
85	At	(210)	Astatine
86	Rn	(222)	Radon
87	Fr	(223)	Francium
88	Ra	226.025	Radium
(89-103)			
104	Rf	(261)	
105	Ha	(262)	
106		(263)	
107		(262)	
109		(266)	

Lanthanide series

Atomic number	Symbol	Atomic weight*	Name
57	La	138.906	Lanthanum
58	Ce	140.12	Cerium
59	Pr	140.91	Praseodymium
60	Nd	144.24	Neodymium
61	Pm	(145)	Promethium
62	Sm	150.35	Samarium
63	Eu	152.0	Europium
64	Gd	157.25	Gadolinium
65	Tb	158.93	Terbium
66	Dy	162.50	Dysprosium
67	Ho	164.93	Holmium
68	Er	167.26	Erbium
69	Tm	168.94	Thulium
70	Yb	173.04	Ytterbium
71	Lu	174.97	Lutetium

Actinide series

Atomic number	Symbol	Atomic weight*	Name
89	Ac	227.028	Actinium
90	Th	232.038	Thorium
91	Pa	231.036	Protoactinium
92	U	238.029	Uranium
93	Np	237.048	Neptunium
94	Pu	(244)	Plutonium
95	Am	(243)	Americium
96	Cm	(247)	Curium
97	Bk	(247)	Berkelium
98	Cf	(251)	Californium
99	Es	(252)	Einsteinium
100	Fm	(257)	Fermium
101	Md	(258)	Mendelevium
102	No	(259)	Nobelium
103	Lr	(260)	Lawrencium

* Parentheses around atomic weight indicate that the weight given is that of the most stable known isotope.

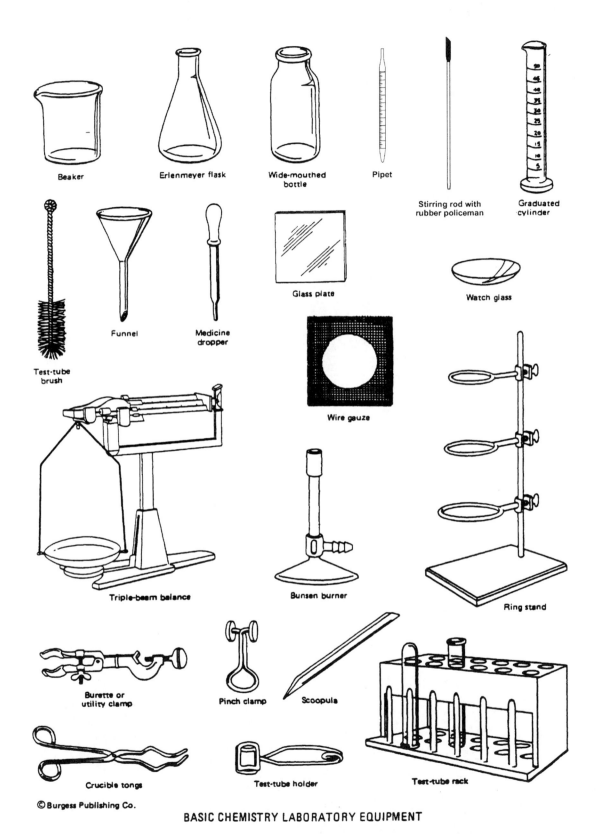

Beaker

Erlenmeyer flask

Wide-mouthed bottle

Pipet

Stirring rod with rubber policeman

Graduated cylinder

Test-tube brush

Funnel

Medicine dropper

Glass plate

Watch glass

Wire gauze

Triple-beam balance

Bunsen burner

Ring stand

Burette or utility clamp

Pinch clamp

Scoopula

Crucible tongs

Test-tube holder

Test-tube rack

© Burgess Publishing Co.

BASIC CHEMISTRY LABORATORY EQUIPMENT

From *Fundamentals of Chemistry in the Laboratory,* Fourth Edition, Ralph A. Burns. Copyright © 2003 by Pearson Education, Inc. All rights reserved.

Experiment 1

Experiment 1

Instrumental Measurements

- To obtain measurements of length, mass, volume, temperature, and time.
- To determine the mass and volume of an unknown rectangular solid.
- To gain proficiency in using the following instruments: metric rulers, balances, graduated cylinder, thermometer, and clock.

DISCUSSION

The **metric system** uses a basic set of units and prefixes. The basic unit of length is the meter, the basic unit of mass is the gram, and the basic unit of volume is the liter. Metric prefixes make these basic units larger or smaller by powers of 10. For example, a kilometer is a thousand times longer than a meter, and a millimeter is a thousand times less than a meter. In the laboratory, the most common unit of length is **centimeter** (symbol **cm**), the most common unit of mass is **gram** (symbol **g**), and the most common unit of volume is **milliliter** (symbol **mL**).

Scientific instruments have gradually progressed to a high state of sensitivity. However, it is never possible to make an exact measurement. The reason for this is that all instruments possess a degree of **uncertainty**—no matter how sensitive. The amount of uncertainty is shown by the significant digits in the measurement. For example, a metric ruler may measure length to the nearest tenth of a centimeter (± 0.1 cm). A different metric ruler may measure length to the nearest five hundredths of a centimeter (± 0.05 cm). The measurement with the least uncertainty is the most exact; that is, ± 0.05 cm.

In this experiment, we will become familiar with several instruments. We will make measurements of **mass** with balances having progressively greater sensitivity. A decigram balance is so named because the uncertainty is one-tenth of a gram ($\pm$ 0.1 g). It follows that the uncertainty of a centigram balance is one-hundredth of a gram ($\pm$ 0.01 g), and a milligram balance has an uncertainty of one-thousandth of a gram ($\pm$ 0.001 g). Table 1 lists basic units and symbols for the metric system.

Table 1 Metric Units of Length, Mass, and Volume

Physical Quantity	Basic Unit	Multiple/Fraction of Basic Unit	Derived Unit	Symbol of Derived Unit
length	meter	1000 (10^3)	kilometer	km
		0.1 (10^{-1})	decimeter	dm
		0.01 (10^{-2})	centimeter	cm
		0.001 (10^{-3})	millimeter	mm
mass	gram	1000 (10^3)	kilogram	kg
		0.1 (10^{-1})	decigram	dg
		0.01 (10^{-2})	centigram	cg
		0.001 (10^{-3})	milligram	mg
volume	liter	1000 (10^3)	kiloliter	kL
		0.1 (10^{-1})	deciliter	dL
		0.01 (10^{-2})	centiliter	cL
		0.001 (10^{-3})	milliliter	mL

We will make length measurements using metric rulers that differ in their uncertainty. METRIC RULER A is calibrated in 1-cm divisions and has an uncertainty of $\pm$ 0.1 cm. METRIC RULER B has 0.1-cm subdivisions and an uncertainty of $\pm$ 0.05 cm. Thus, METRIC RULER B has less uncertainty than METRIC RULER A. The following examples demonstrate measurement of length utilizing the two different metric rulers.

Example Exercise 1 • Metric Ruler Measurements

A copper rod is measured with the metric ruler shown below. What is the length of the rod?

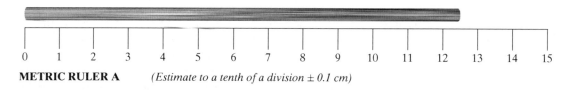

0 1 2 3 4 5 6 7 8 9 10 11 12 13 14 15

METRIC RULER A   *(Estimate to a tenth of a division $\pm$ 0.1 cm)*

Solution: Each division represents one centimeter. The end of the rod lies between the 12th and 13th divisions. We can estimate to a tenth of a division ($\pm$ 0.1 cm). Since the end of the rod lies about five-tenths past 12, we can estimate the length as

$$12 \text{ cm} + 0.5 \text{ cm} = 12.5 \text{ cm}$$

Example Exercise 2 • Metric Ruler Measurements

The same copper rod is measured with the metric ruler shown below. What is the length of the rod?

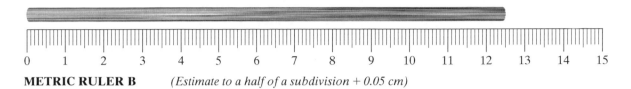

METRIC RULER B   *(Estimate to a half of a subdivision ± 0.05 cm)*

Solution: Note that this ruler is divided into centimeters that are subdivided into tenths of centimeters. The end of the rod lies between the 12th and 13th divisions and between the 5th and 6th subdivisions. Thus, the length is between 12.5 cm and 12.6 cm.

We can estimate the measurement more precisely. A subdivision is too small to divide into ten parts but we can estimate to half of a subdivision (±0.05 cm). The length is 12 cm + 0.5 cm + 0.05 cm = 12.55 cm.

We can measure the volume of a liquid using a graduated cylinder. If we carefully examine the 100-mL graduated cylinder shown in Figure 1, we notice that it is marked in 10-mL intervals that have ten subdivisions. Therefore, each subdivision equals one milliliter. If we estimate to half of a subdivision, the volume has an uncertainty of ± 0.5 mL.

When reading a graduated cylinder, read the bottom of the meniscus. The **meniscus** is the lens-shaped surface of the liquid. Also, you should observe the meniscus at eye level in order to avoid a reading error.

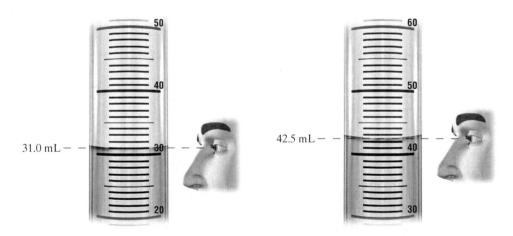

Figure 1 Graduated Cylinder Example readings using proper eye position
and recording the bottom of the meniscus to half a subdivision (± 0.5 mL).

We can measure the temperature using a Celsius thermometer. If we examine the thermometer shown in Figure 2, we notice that it is marked in 10°C intervals that have ten subdivisions. Thus, each subdivision equals one degree Celsius. If we estimate to half of a subdivision, the temperature measurement has an uncertainty of ± 0.5°C.

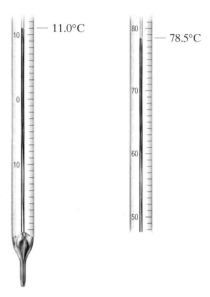

Figure 2 Celsius Thermometer Example readings obtained using a Celsius thermometer and recording the top of the liquid to half a subdivision (± 0.5°C).

Table 2 indicates the uncertainty for each of the instruments utilized in this experiment. Moreover, some example readings are provided that are similar to actual measurements taken during the experiment.

Table 2 Measurement of Length, Mass, Volume, Temperature, and Time

Physical Quantity	Measuring Instrument	Measurement Uncertainty	Example Reading
length	metric ruler A	± 0.1 cm	5.2 cm, 10.1 cm
	metric ruler B	± 0.05 cm	5.20 cm, 10.05 cm
mass	decigram balance	± 0.1 g	86.4 g, 101.7 g
	centigram balance	± 0.01 g	86.32 g, 101.73 g
	milligram balance	± 0.001 g	86.318 g, 101.730 g
volume	graduated cylinder	± 0.5 mL	27.5 mL, 60.0 mL
temperature	thermometer	± 0.5°C	1.0°C, 23.5°C
time	sweep-second clock	± 1 s	45 s, 52 s
	digital watch	± 0.01 s	45.31 s, 51.95 s

To test your skill in making metric measurements, we will find the mass and volume of an unknown rectangular solid. The volume of a rectangular solid is calculated by multiplying its length, width, and thickness. The following examples will illustrate.

Example Exercise 3   •   Volume of a Rectangular Solid

An unknown rectangular solid was measured with METRIC RULER A, which provided the following dimensions: 5.0 cm by 2.5 cm by 1.1 cm. What is the volume of the solid?

Solution: The volume of a rectangular solid is equal to its length times width times thickness.

$$5.0 \text{ cm} \times 2.5 \text{ cm} \times 1.1 \text{ cm} = 13.75 \text{ cm}^3 = 14 \text{ cm}^3$$

In multiplication, the product is limited by the least number of significant digits. In this example, each dimension has two significant digits; thus, the volume is limited to two significant digits.

Example Exercise 4   •   Volume of a Rectangular Solid

The unknown rectangular solid was measured with METRIC RULER B, which provided the following dimensions: 5.00 cm by 2.45 cm by 1.15 cm. What is the volume of the solid?

Solution: The volume is once again found by multiplying the three dimensions.

$$5.00 \text{ cm} \times 2.45 \text{ cm} \times 1.15 \text{ cm} = 14.0875 \text{ cm}^3 = 14.1 \text{ cm}^3$$

In this example, each dimension has three significant digits; thus, the volume has three significant digits.

EQUIPMENT and CHEMICALS

- decigram balance
- centigram balance
- milligram balance
- 125-mL Erlenmeyer flask
- crucible and cover
- watchglass
- evaporating dish
- dropper pipet
- 13 × 100 mm test tubes (3) and test tube rack

- 110°C thermometer
- 150-mL beaker
- ice
- ring stand
- wire gauze
- Solution A, (2 g KIO_3/L)
- Solution B, (dissolve 1 g starch in 1 L of boiling water; add 0.4 g $NaHSO_3$, 5 mL 1 M H_2SO_4)
- unknown rectangular solids
- nickel (5¢ coin)

PROCEDURE

A. Length Measurement

1. Measure the diameter of a watchglass with each of the following: (a) METRIC RULER A, (b) METRIC RULER B.

2. Measure the diameter of an evaporating dish with each of the following: (a) METRIC RULER A, (b) METRIC RULER B.

    Note: Do not include the spout when measuring the evaporating dish.

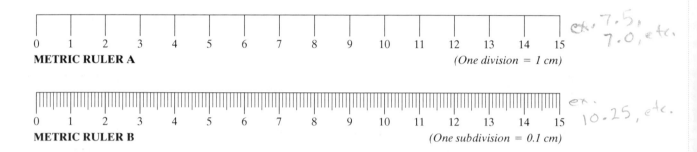

Figure 3 Metric Rulers The uncertainty of METRIC RULER A is a tenth of a division (± 0.1 cm), and METRIC RULER B is half of a subdivision (± 0.05 cm).

B. Mass Measurement

1. Determine the mass of a 125-mL Erlenmeyer flask on each of the following balances: (a) decigram balance, (b) centigram balance, (c) milligram balance.

2. Determine the mass of a crucible and cover on each of the three balances.

    Note: Refer to balance instructions in the Platform Balance, Beam Balance, and Electronic Balance Appendices if they are included in your lab manual. The instructor may omit one or more of the above weighings according to the availability of decigram, centigram, and milligram balances.

C. Volume Measurement

1. Fill a 100-mL graduated cylinder with water. Adjust the bottom of the meniscus to the full mark with a dropper pipet. Record the volume as 100.0 mL.

2. Fill a 13 × 100 mm test tube with water from the graduated cylinder. Record the new meniscus reading in the graduated cylinder (± 0.5 mL).

3. Fill a second test tube with water. Record the volume in the graduated cylinder.

4. Fill a third test tube with water. Record the volume in the graduated cylinder.

D. Temperature Measurement

1. Record the temperature in the laboratory using a Celsius thermometer ($\pm 0.5°C$).

2. Half fill a 100-mL beaker with ice and water. Insert the thermometer into the beaker, and record the coldest observed temperature ($\pm 0.5°C$).

3. Half fill a 150-mL beaker with distilled water. Support the beaker on a ring stand with a wire gauze as shown in Figure 4. Heat the water to boiling with a laboratory burner. Shut off the burner and record the hottest observed temperature ($\pm 0.5°C$).

   Note: Hold the thermometer off the bottom of the beaker to avoid an erroneously high reading. Refer to the laboratory burner instructions in the Laboratory Burner Appendix if it is included in your lab manual.

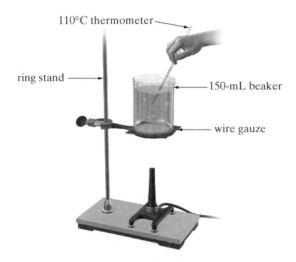

Figure 4 Temperature of Boiling Water To avoid breakage,
do not allow the thermometer to touch the hot glass beaker.

E. Time Measurement

1. Fill one test tube with Solution A and a second test tube with Solution B. Pour both solutions simultaneously into a 150-mL beaker. Record the number of seconds for a reaction to occur; this is indicated by a color change.

F. Mass and Volume of an Unknown Solid

1. Obtain a rectangular solid, and record the unknown number in the Data Table. Find the mass of the unknown rectangular solid using each of the following: (a) a decigram balance, (b) a centigram balance, and (c) a milligram balance.

2. Measure the length, width, and thickness of the rectangular solid unknown using METRIC RULER A in Figure 3. Calculate the volume.

3. Measure the length, width, and thickness of the rectangular solid unknown using METRIC FIGURE B in Figure 3. Calculate the volume.

G. Metric Estimations

1. Estimate the mass of a nickel to the nearest gram. Weigh the nickel on any balance and record the mass ± 1g.

2. Estimate the diameter of a nickel to the nearest centimeter. Measure the nickel with any metric ruler and record the length ± 1cm.

3. Estimate the volume of 20 drops of water to the nearest milliliter. Using a dropper pipet, add 20 drops of water into a graduated cylinder and record the volume ± 1mL.

PRELABORATORY ASSIGNMENT*

1. In your own words, define the following terms:

   centimeter (cm)

   gram (g)

   mass

   meniscus

   metric system

   milliliter (mL)

   uncertainty

2. Identify the following laboratory equipment: beaker, crucible and cover, evaporating dish, Erlenmeyer flask, graduated cylinder, test tube, thermometer, watchglass, wire gauze.

3. State the physical quantity expressed by each of the following measurements.

   (a) 25.0 cm   (b) 25.0 g

   (c) 25.0 mL   (d) 25.0°C

   (e) 25.0 s

4. State the uncertainty in the following measuring instruments.

   (a) METRIC RULER A   (b) METRIC RULER B

   (c) decigram balance   (d) centigram balance

   (e) milligram balance   (f) graduated cylinder

   (g) thermometer   (h) sweep-second clock

---

*Answers at the end of the experiment.

5. Record the measurement indicated by each of the following instruments.

(a) metric rulers

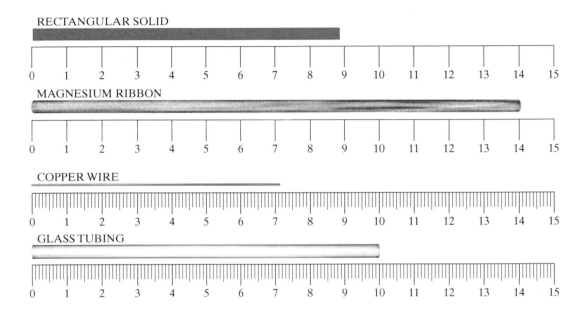

(b) graduated cylinders

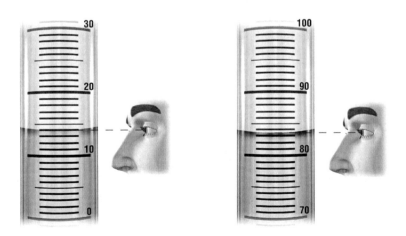

(c) thermometers

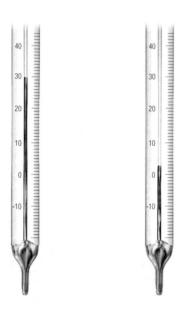

6. An unknown rectangular solid has the following measurements: 3.7 cm by 2.4 cm by 1.3 cm. Calculate the volume in cubic centimeters.

7. An unknown rectangular solid has the following measurements: 3.70 cm by 2.45 cm by 1.25 cm. Calculate the volume in cubic centimeters.

8. What safety precautions must be observed in this experiment?

Answers to
Prelaboratory Assignment

INSTRUMENTAL MEASUREMENTS

1. See the Glossary.

2. Refer to the diagrams of Common Laboratory Equipment.

3. (a) length   (b) mass   (c) volume   (d) temperature   (e) time

4. (a) ± 0.1 cm   (b) ± 0.05 cm   (c) ± 0.1 g   (d) ± 0.01 g   (e) ± 0.001 g   (f) ± 0.5 mL;

   (g) ± 0.5°C   (h) ± 1 s

5. (a) 8.8 cm, 14.0 cm, 7.15 cm; 10.00 cm; (b) 14.0 mL, 83.5 mL; (c) 30.0°C, 2.5°C

6. $11.544 = 12 \text{ cm}^3$

7. $11.33125 = 11.3 \text{ cm}^3$

8. • Handle balances carefully, as they are sensitive instruments.

   • Handle the laboratory burner and boiling waterbath carefully, as they can cause burns.

   • Handle the thermometer carefully, as it is easily broken and can cause cuts. (Report a broken thermometer immediately to the Instructor; mercury vapor is poisonous.)

Experiment 2

Experiment 2

Density of Liquids and Solids

OBJECTIVES

- To observe the relative densities of some common liquids and solids.
- To determine the densities of water, an unknown liquid, a rubber stopper, and an unknown rectangular solid.
- To determine the thickness of a piece of aluminum foil using the density concept.
- To gain proficiency in performing the following experimental procedures: pipetting a liquid, weighing by difference, and determining a volume by displacement.

DISCUSSION

Density is a physical property of liquids and solids. We can define **density** (symbol *d*) as the amount of mass in a given volume. To determine the density of a solid experimentally, we must measure the mass of the solid using a balance. To determine the mass of a liquid, we use an indirect technique called **weighing by difference** (Figure 1). First, we weigh a flask empty. Second, we add a given volume of liquid into the flask and reweigh. The mass of the liquid is found by subtracting the first and second weighings.

After collecting the experimental data, we can calculate density by dividing the mass by the volume. It is important, however, that we attach the proper units to the calculated value. The density of liquids and solids is usually expressed in grams per milliliter (g/mL) or grams per cubic centimeter (g/cm^3). Since 1 mL = 1 cm^3, the numberial value for density in g/mL and g/cm^3 is identical. For example, the density of water may be expressed as 1.00 g/mL or 1.00 g/cm^3.

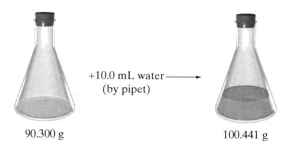

90.300 g   100.441 g

Figure 1 Weighing by Difference The mass of the liquid is
found by the difference in masses: 100.441 g – 90.300 g = 10.141 g.

Example Exercise 1   •   Density of a Liquid

A 10.0-mL sample of water is pipetted into a flask. The mass of water, 10.141 g, is found after weighing by difference (see Figure 1). Calculate the density of water.

Solution: Dividing the mass of water by volume, we have

$$\frac{10.141 \text{ g}}{10.0 \text{ mL}} = 1.01 \text{ g/mL}$$

We round the answer to three significant digits because there are only three digits in the denominator. In this example, the calculated value, 1.01 g/mL, agrees closely with the theoretical value, 1.00 g/mL. The slight discrepancy is due to experimental error.

The volume of an irregular object cannot be found directly. However, its volume can be found indirectly from the amount of water it displaces. This technique is called **volume by displacement**. For example, the volume of a rubber stopper can be determined as shown in Figure 2. The initial reading of water in the graduated cylinder is observed. The stopper is introduced into the graduated cylinder and the final reading is recorded. The difference between the initial and final readings corresponds to the volume of water displaced. The volume of water displaced is equal to the volume of the rubber stopper.

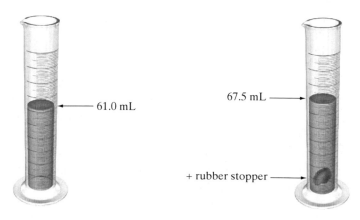

Figure 2 Volume by Displacement The volume of the rubber stopper is found by the increase in volume:
67.5 mL – 61.0 mL = 6.5 mL.

Example Exercise 2 • **Density of a Rubber Stopper**

A rubber stopper weighing 8.453 g displaces 6.5 mL of water in a graduated cylinder (Figure 2). What is the density of the rubber stopper?

Solution: Dividing the mass of the rubber stopper by its volume, we have

$$\frac{8.453 \text{ g}}{6.5 \text{ mL}} = 1.3 \text{ g/mL}$$

In this example, the volume has only two digits. Thus, the density is limited to two significant digits.

We will also determine the density of a solid. The volume of any solid object with regular dimensions can be found by calculation. For example, the volume of a rectangular solid object is calculated by multiplying its length times its width times its thickness.

Example Exercise 3 • **Density of a Rectangular Solid**

The mass of an unknown rectangular block is 139.443 g. If the block measures 5.00 cm by 2.55 cm by 1.25 cm, what is its density?

Solution: First, we calculate the volume of the rectangular block.

$$5.00 \text{ cm} \times 2.55 \text{ cm} \times 1.25 \text{ cm} = 15.9 \text{ cm}^3$$

Second, we find the density of the unknown rectangular solid.

$$\frac{139.443 \text{ g}}{15.9 \text{ cm}^3} = 8.77 \text{ g/cm}^3$$

The thickness of a sheet of metal foil is too thin to measure with a ruler. However, we can find the thickness indirectly by calculation. Given the mass, length, and width of a metal foil, we can use the density of the metal to calculate the thickness of the foil.

Example Exercise 4 • **Thickness of a Metal Foil**

A sheet of tin foil has a mass of 0.571 g and measures 5.10 cm by 10.25 cm. Given the density of tin, 7.28 g/cm³, calculate the thickness of the foil.

Solution: To calculate the thickness of the foil, we must first find the volume. The volume can be calculated using a density factor as follows.

$$0.571 \text{ g} \times \frac{1 \text{ cm}^3}{7.28 \text{ g}} = 0.0784 \text{ cm}^3$$

The thickness is found after dividing the volume by its length and width.

$$\frac{0.0784 \text{ cm}^3}{(5.10 \text{ cm})(10.25 \text{ cm})} = 0.00150 \text{ cm} \ (1.50 \times 10^{-3} \text{ cm})$$

EQUIPMENT and CHEMICALS

A. Instructor Demonstrations

- tall glass cylinder
- methylene chloride (optional)
- hexane

- glass marble
- rubber stopper
- ice
- cork

B–F. Student Experiments

- 125-mL Erlenmeyer flask with stopper
- 150-mL beaker
- 10-mL pipet
- pipet bulb
- 100-mL beaker

- 100-mL graduated cylinder
- #2 rubber stopper
- unknown liquids
- unknown rectangular solids
- aluminum foil, ~ 5 × 10 cm rectangle

PROCEDURE

A. Instructor Demonstration

1. Half fill a tall glass cylinder with water. Add methylene chloride until two layers are observed. Add hexane until three layers are observed. Record the positions of each layer in the Data Table.

   Note: The instructor may wish to point out a waste container for chemicals, such as methylene chloride, that should not be poured into the sink.

2. Drop a glass marble into the tall glass cylinder. Record the observation.

3. Drop a rubber stopper into the tall glass cylinder. Record the observation.

4. Drop a piece of ice into the tall glass cylinder. Record the observation.

5. Drop a cork into the tall glass cylinder. Record the observation.

B. Density of Water

1. Weigh a 125-mL Erlenmeyer flask fitted with a rubber stopper.

2. Half fill a 150-mL beaker with distilled water, and pipet 10.0 mL into the 125-mL flask.

3. Reweigh the flask and stopper, and determine the mass of water by difference.

4. Repeat a second trial for the density of the water.

   Note: It is not necessary to dry the flask between trials because the 10.0-mL sample of water is weighed by difference.

5. Calculate the density of the water for each trial, and report the average value for both trials.

C. Density of an Unknown Liquid

1. Obtain about 25 mL of an unknown liquid in a 100-mL beaker. Record the unknown number in the Data Table.

2. Weigh a 125-mL Erlenmeyer flask fitted with a rubber stopper.

3. Condition the pipet, and transfer 10.0-mL of unknown liquid into the flask.

4. Reweigh the flask and stopper, and determine the mass of liquid by difference.

5. Repeat a second trial for the density of the unknown liquid.

6. Calculate the density of the liquid for each trial, and report the average value for both trials.

D. Density of a Rubber Stopper

1. Weigh a dry #2 rubber stopper.

2. Half fill a 100-mL graduated cylinder with water. Record the water level by observing the bottom of the meniscus and estimating to ± 0.5 mL.

3. Tilt the graduated cylinder, and let the stopper slowly slide into the water. Record the new level, and calculate the volume by displacement for the stopper.

4. Repeat a second trial for the density of the rubber stopper.

5. Calculate the density of the rubber stopper for each trial, and report the average value for both trials.

E. Density of an Unknown Solid

1. Obtain a rectangular solid, and record the unknown number in the Data Table.

2. Weigh the unknown solid, and record the mass.

3. Measure and record the length, width, and thickness of the unknown rectangular solid, using the metric ruler in Figure 3.

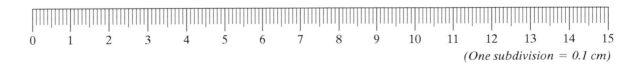

(One subdivision = 0.1 cm)

Figure 3 Metric Ruler The uncertainty of the measurement is ± 0.05 cm.

4. Calculate the volume of the unknown rectangular solid.

5. Repeat a second trial for the volume of the unknown solid using a different balance and the metric ruler in Figure 3.

F. Thickness of Aluminum Foil

1. Obtain a rectangular piece of aluminum foil.

2. Record the length and width of the foil (see Figure 3) in the Data Table.

3. Fold the foil twice. Weigh and record its mass.

4. Calculate the volume and thickness of the aluminum foil ($d = 2.70$ g/cm^3).

Density of Liquids and Solids

NAME _____

DATE _____   SECTION _____

1. In your own words, define the following terms:

    conditioning

    density

    meniscus

    volume by displacement

    weighing by difference

2. Record the volume of liquid shown in each of the following graduated cylinders.

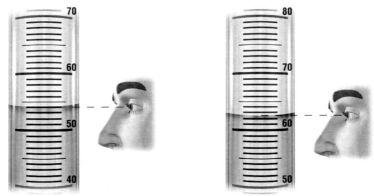

3. Record the length of the rectangular solid shown next to the following metric rulers.

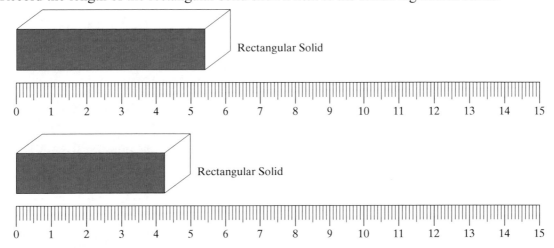

*Answers at the end of the experiment.

4. A 10.0-mL sample of acetone is pipetted into a flask with stopper. The mass is found by difference to be 7.899 g. Calculate the density of the liquid.

5. A piece of chalk weighing 15.600 g displaces 6.5 mL of water in a graduated cylinder. Calculate the density of the chalk.

6 A rectangular block of jade has a mass of 146.25 g and measures 10.00 cm by 3.00 cm by 1.50 cm. What is the density of the jade?

7. Find the thickness of a piece of gold foil that has a mass of 1.000 g and measures 5.00 cm by 10.00 cm. The density of gold is 18.9 g/cm^3.

8. What safety precautions must be observed in this experiment?

Density of Liquids and Solids

NAME _____

DATE _____   SECTION _____

DATA TABLE

A. Instructor Demonstration   *Observations*

     water added to cylinder

     methylene chloride added to water

     hexane added to water

     glass marble added to cylinder

     rubber stopper added to cylinder

     ice added to cylinder

     cork added to cylinder

Diagram of the Tall Glass Cylinder

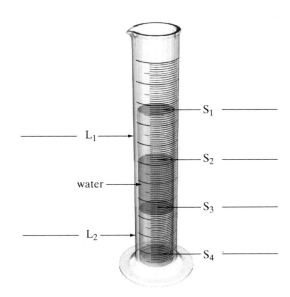

B. Density of Water

    mass of flask and stopper + water   _____ g   _____ g

    mass of flask and stopper   _____ g   _____ g

    mass of water   _____ g   _____ g

    volume of water   _____ mL   _____ mL

Show the calculation for the density of water for trial 1 (see Example Exercise 1).

    Density of water   _____ g/mL   _____ g/mL

      Average density of water   _____ g/mL

C. Density of an Unknown Liquid   **UNKNOWN #** _____

    mass of flask and stopper + liquid   _____ g   _____ g

    mass of flask and stopper   _____ g   _____ g

    mass of unknown liquid   _____ g   _____ g

    volume of unknown liquid   _____ mL   _____ mL

Show the calculation for the density of the unknown liquid for trial 1.

    Density of unknown liquid   _____ g/mL   _____ g/mL

      Average density of unknown liquid   _____ g/mL

D. Density of a Rubber Stopper

mass of a rubber stopper   _____ g   _____ g

final cylinder reading   _____ mL   _____ mL

initial cylinder reading   _____ mL   _____ mL

volume of rubber stopper   _____ mL   _____ mL

Show the calculation of density for the stopper for trial 1 (see Example Exercise 2).

Density of rubber stopper   _____ g/mL   _____ g/mL

Average density of rubber stopper   _____ g/mL

E. Density of an Unknown Solid   **UNKNOWN #** _____

mass of solid   _____ g   _____ g

length of solid   _____ cm   _____ cm

width of solid   _____ cm   _____ cm

thickness of solid   _____ cm   _____ cm

Show the calculation for the volume of the unknown for trial 1 (see Example Exercise 3).

volume of solid   _____ cm^3 _____ cm^3

Show the calculation for the density of the unknown for trial 1 (see Example Exercise 3).

Density of rectangular solid   _____ g/cm^3 _____ g/cm^3

Average density of the solid   _____ g/cm^3

F. Thickness of Aluminum Foil

    length of foil   _____ cm

    width of foil   _____ cm

    mass of foil   _____ g

Show the calculation for the volume of the aluminum foil, $d = 2.70$ g/cm^3 (see Example Exercise 4).

    Volume of foil   _____ cm^3

Show the calculation for the thickness of the foil in centimeters.

    Thickness of foil   _____ cm

Answers to
Prelaboratory Assignment

DENSITY OF LIQUIDS AND SOLIDS

1. See the Glossary.

2. 54.0 mL, 62.5 mL

3. 5.40 cm, 4.25 cm

4. 0.790 g/mL

5. 2.4 g/mL

6. 3.25 g/cm^3

7. 0.00106 cm (1.06 $\times$ 10^{-3} cm)

8. • Handle balances carefully, as they are sensitive instruments.
   • Handle a pipet carefully, as it can easily snap and cause cuts.
   • Keep the unknown organic liquid away from a laboratory burner flame.

Experiment 3

Experiment 4

Experiment 4

Physical Properties and Chemical Properties

OBJECTIVES

- To observe the appearance of several metals and nonmetals.
- To determine the boiling points of methanol and an unknown liquid.
- To determine whether a solid is soluble or insoluble in water.
- To determine whether a liquid is soluble or insoluble in water.
- To determine whether a substance is undergoing a physical or chemical change.
- To gain experience in determining a boiling point and observing test tube reactions.

DISCUSSION

Chemists classify matter according to its physical and chemical properties. Matter can be classified as a mixture or a pure substance, depending upon its properties. A **heterogeneous mixture** has physical and chemical properties that vary within the sample. For example, combining sugar and salt gives a heterogeneous mixture because the properties of sugar and salt are different.

A **homogeneous mixture** has constant properties although the properties can vary from sample to sample. A homogeneous mixture may be a gaseous mixture, a solution, or an alloy. Examples include air, seawater, and brass, which is an alloy of the metals copper and zinc.

A pure **substance** is either an **element** or a **compound**; all substances have constant and predictable properties. Examples include the compound sodium chloride, as well as the elements sodium metal and chlorine gas.

Sugar is a compound that contains the elements carbon, hydrogen, and oxygen. When heated, sugar decomposes into black carbon and water vapor. When electricity is passed through water, it decomposes into elemental hydrogen and oxygen gases. Although hydrogen and oxygen are both colorless, odorless gases, they differ in their other physical and chemical properties. Figure 1 illustrates the overall relationship for the classification of matter.

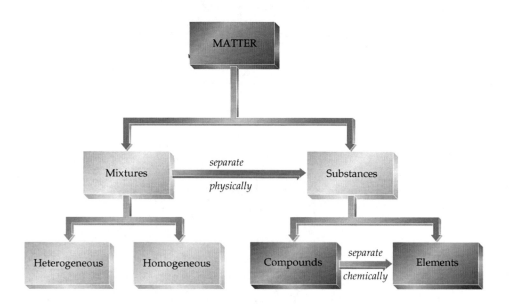

Figure 1 Classification of Matter Matter is either a mixture or a pure substance. The properties of a heterogeneous mixture vary within the sample. The properties of a homogeneous mixture are constant but vary from sample to sample. A substance maybe either a compound or an element, but the properties of a substance are predictable and constant.

A **physical property** refers to a characteristic that can be observed without changing the composition of the substance. A partial list of physical properties that are usually considered important include: physical state (solid, liquid, gas), crystalline structure (crystals or powder), color, density, malleability, ductility, melting point, boiling point, electrical conductivity, heat conductivity, and solubility in water.

A **chemical property** refers to a characteristic that can be observed only while changing the composition of the substance. We refer to a change in composition as a chemical reaction. A freshly sliced apple turning brown, an antacid tablet fizzing in water, and food releasing an unpleasant aroma, are all familiar and practical examples of a chemical change.

In this experiment, we will observe a **physical change** as a substance undergoes a temporary color change, changes physical state, or gives no reaction after combining two solutions. We will observe a **chemical change** as a substance undergoes a permanent color change, releases a gas, or forms an insoluble substance after combining two solutions.

EQUIPMENT and CHEMICALS

- ring stand
- wire gauze
- 400-mL beaker
- 16 × 150 mm test tube
- boiling chips
- 110°C thermometer
- split cork
- 13 × 100 mm test tubes (6) and test tube rack
- crucible tongs
- 250-mL beaker
- evaporating dish
- test tube brush
- test tube holder
- wash bottle with distilled water

- small vials with samples of cobalt, hydrogen, magnesium, manganese, neon, oxygen, silicon, sulfur, tin, zinc
- methyl alcohol, CH_3OH
- boiling point unknowns
- iodine, solid crystals I_2
- sucrose, solid crystals $C_{12}H_{22}O_{11}$
- amyl alcohol, $C_5H_{11}OH$
- copper wire, heavy gauge Cu
- ammonium bicarbonate, solid NH_4HCO_3
- potassium bicarbonate, solid $KHCO_3$
- sodium carbonate solution, 0.5 M Na_2CO_3
- sodium sulfate solution, 0.1 M Na_2SO_4
- dilute hydrochloric acid, 6 M HCl
- calcium nitrate solution, 0.1 M $Ca(NO_3)_2$
- copper(II) nitrate solution, 0.1 M $Cu(NO_3)_2$
- ammonium hydroxide solution, 6 $M \cdot NH_4OH$

PROCEDURE

A. Physical Properties

1. *Physical State and Color*

   Observe vials of the following elements and record your observations in the Data Table. Classify the element as a metal, a nonmetal, or a semimetal.

   (a) cobalt   (b) hydrogen
   (c) magnesium   (d) manganese
   (e) neon   (f) oxygen
   (g) silicon   (h) sulfur
   (i) tin   (j) zinc

2. *Boiling Point*

   (a) Place a 400-mL beaker on a wire gauze, and support it on a ring stand. Add 300 mL of water to the beaker, bring to a boil, and then shut off the burner. Put about 20 drops of methyl alcohol into a 16 × 150 mm test tube. Add a boiling chip and place the test tube in the beaker of water. Suspend a thermometer about 1 cm above the liquid. Allow the alcohol to boil in the waterbath for a couple of minutes. Record the temperature (± 0.5°C) when the condensed alcohol vapor begins dripping from the tip of the thermometer (Figure 2).

   Caution: Methyl alcohol is flammable, and the vapors must not be near the flame of a laboratory burner.

   (b) Record the number of an unknown liquid, and determine the boiling point of the liquid (± 0.5°C) as above.

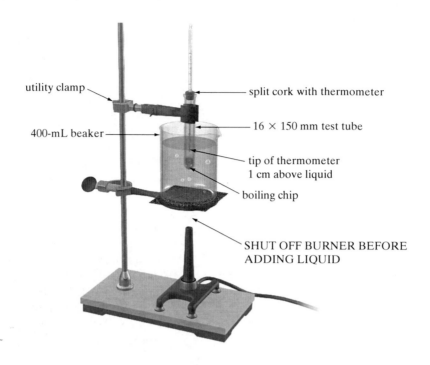

utility clamp

split cork with thermometer

400-mL beaker

16 × 150 mm test tube

tip of thermometer
1 cm above liquid

boiling chip

SHUT OFF BURNER BEFORE
ADDING LIQUID

Figure 2 Boiling Point Apparatus The boiling point is recorded when the gaseous vapor
condenses to a liquid and begins to drip from the tip of the thermometer.

3. *Solubility of a Solid in Water*

   Add 10 drops of distilled water in two test tubes. Place a small crystal of iodine in one test tube
   and a crystal of sucrose (table sugar) in the other. Shake the test tubes briefly to dissolve the
   crystals. State whether each solid is *soluble* or *insoluble* in water.

4. *Solubility of a Liquid in Water*

   Add 10 drops of distilled water in two test tubes. Add a few drops of methyl alcohol to one test tube
   and amyl alcohol to the other. Shake the test tubes briefly to mix the liquids. State whether each
   liquid is *soluble* or *insoluble* in water.

B. Chemical Properties

   1. *Reactions of Elements*

      (a) Inspect a piece of copper wire. Hold the wire with crucible tongs, and heat the wire until it
          glows red. Allow the wire to cool and inspect once again. Classify your observation as a *physical change* or a *chemical change*.

      (b) Place a few small crystals of iodine in a dry 250-mL beaker. Cover the beaker with an evaporating dish and place ice in the dish (Figure 3). Support the beaker on a ring stand, and heat the
          iodine slowly until all the crystals vaporize and the vapor deposits on the bottom of the evaporating dish. Classify your observation as a *physical change* or a *chemical change*.

Signs of chemical reactions
- gas formation
- change in color
- solid forming in liquid (precipitate)
- flame

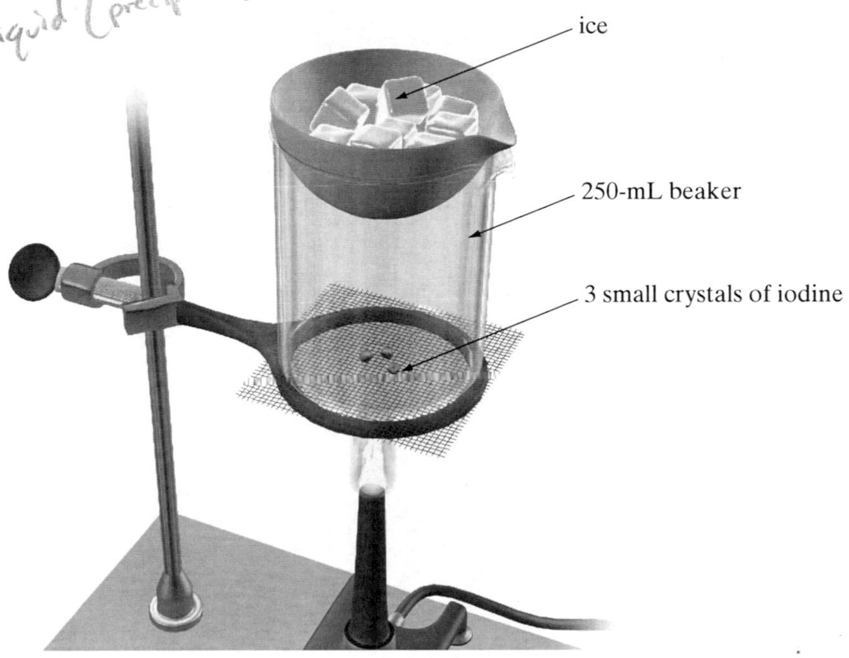

Figure 3 Apparatus for Sublimation/Deposition A few small crystals of iodine are placed in the beaker and heated gently. The gaseous iodine vapor is collected on the bottom of the evaporating dish.

2. *Reactions of Compounds*

   Put a pea-sized portion of ammonium bicarbonate into one test tube and potasium bicarbonate into another. Using a test tube holder, heat each test tube gently and note the aroma or odor. Classify your observation as a *physical change* or a *chemical change.*

   Caution: When heating a test tube, point the open end in a safe direction.

3. *Reactions of Solutions*

   (a) Put 10 drops of sodium carbonate in a test tube and 10 drops of sodium sulfate in a separate test tube. Add several drops of dilute hydrochloric acid to each test tube, and record any changes. Classify your observation as a *physical change* or a *chemical change.*

   Note: The absence of a reaction is an example of a *physical change* because the physical properties of mass and volume have increased.

   (b) Put 10 drops of calcium nitrate in a test tube and 10 drops of copper(II) nitrate in a separate test tube. Add several drops of dilute ammonium hydroxide to each test tube, and note any changes. Classify your observation as a *physical change* or a *chemical change.*

45

1. In your own words, define the following terms:

   chemical change

   chemical property

   compound

   element

   heterogeneous mixture

   homogeneous mixture

   physical change

   physical property

   substance

2. List several examples of physical properties.

3. List several examples of chemical properties.

4. What is the purpose of the boiling chip when determining the boiling point of a liquid?

5. What experimental observations suggest a chemical change has taken place?

6. What experimental observations suggest a gas is being released?

7. What safety precautions must be observed in this experiment?

---

*Answers at the end of the experiment.

Answers to
Prelaboratory Assignment

PHYSICAL CHANGES AND CHEMICAL CHANGES

1. See the Glossary.

2. Refer to the Discussion section of this experiment.

3. Refer to the Discussion section of this experiment.

4. The boiling chip prevents "bumping," which ejects flammable liquid from the test tube.

5. All of the following suggest a chemical change:

   (1) releasing gas bubbles;   (2) forming an insoluble substance in solution;

   (3) undergoing a permanent color change;   (4) releasing or absorbing energy.

6. A gas is released if there is fizzing or bubbling, or an odor is observed.

7. • Wear goggle eye protection, especially when using the laboratory burner.

   • When determining a boiling point, be careful that the liquid vapors are not near a flame.

   • Avoid breathing iodine vapors (place only 3 small iodine crystals in the beaker), and keep the beaker covered with an evaporating dish while heating the I_2 crystals.

   • Carefully heat a chemical in a test tube, and point the open end in a safe direction.

   • Handle the thermometer carefully, as it is easily broken and can cause cuts. (Report a broken thermometer immediately to the Instructor; mercury vapor is poisonous.)

Experiment 5

Experiment 5

Identifying Anions
in Solution

OBJECTIVES

- To observe the chemical behavior of iodide, chloride, and sulfate ions.
- To analyze an unknown solution for one of more of the following anions: $*^-$, Cl^-, and SO_4^{2-}.
- To develop the following laboratory skills: centrifuging, washing a precipitate, and testing with litmus paper.

DISCUSSION

Qualitative analysis is a systematic procedure for the separation and identification of ions present in an unknown solution. Anion analysis involves the separation and identification of each negatively charged **anion** present in a sample.

If we have an **aqueous solution** containing different anions, it is possible to select a reagent that will form a **precipitate** with one of the anions, but not with the others. We can then use a **centrifuge** to separate the solid particles of precipitate from the aqueous solution. Thus, we separate the anion in the precipitate from the other anions in the original aqueous solution.

For example, we can separate the anions in a solution containing I^-, and SO_4^{2-}, using silver nitrate. The silver ion, Ag^+, precipitates I^- and Cl^-, but gives no reaction with the SO_4^{2-} anion (see Figure 1).

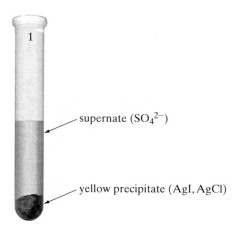

supernate (SO_4^{2-})

yellow precipitate (AgI, AgCl)

Figure 1 Precipitation of AgI and AgCl There is no reaction between
Ag^+ and SO_4^{2-} because Ag_2SO_4 is soluble.

When a silver ion and an aniodide anion are together in the same solution, a precipitate forms because silver iodide, AgI, is insoluble. If sulfate ions are in a solution, no precipitate forms because silver sulfate, Ag_2SO_4, is soluble in water.

In this experiment, you will separate and identify I^-, Cl^-, and SO_4^{2-}. First, a known solution containing all three anions will be analyzed to develop the necessary techniques. Second, an unknown solution with one or more of the three anions will be analyzed to determine the anions present.

Litmus paper can be used to determine whether a solution is acidic or basic. A glass stirring rod is placed in the solution and touched to the litmus paper. Acidic solutions turn blue litmus paper red. Basic solutions turn red litmus paper blue (Figure 2).

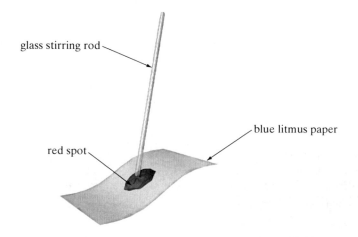

glass stirring rod

red spot

blue litmus paper

Figure 2 Litmus Paper Technique A glass stirring rod is placed in a
solution and touched to blue litmus paper. If the solution is acidic, a red
spot is produced. If the solution is neutral or basic, there is no change.

We will begin the anion analysis with a known solution containing I^-, Cl^-, and SO_4^{2-}. Silver nitrate is added to the known anion solution and the separation begins. Figure 3 present an overview of the analysis. In **Step 1**, I^- is confirmed; in **Step 2**, Cl^- is confirmed; and in **Step 3**, SO_4^{2-} is confirmed.

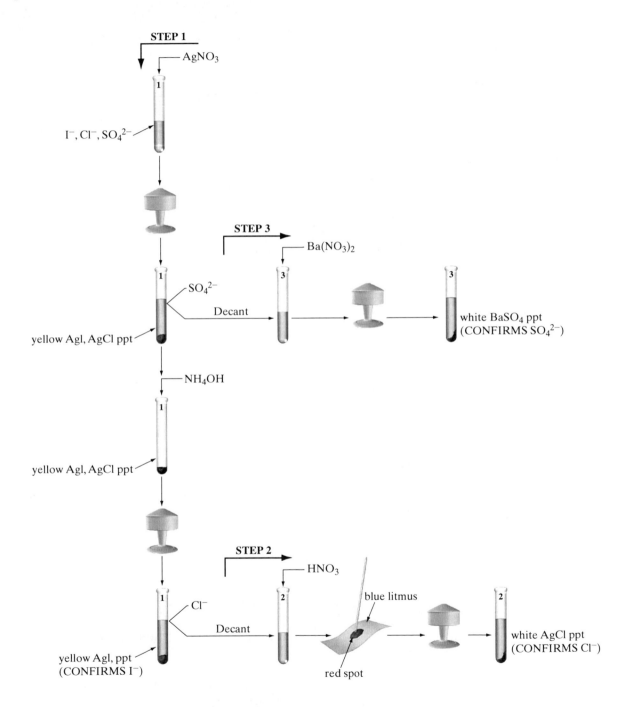

Figure 3 Anion Analysis The systematic separation and identification of I^-, Cl^-, and SO_4^{2-} anions in a known solution.

EQUIPMENT and CHEMICALS

- 13 × 100 mm test tubes (3) and test tube rack
- thin glass stirring rod
- wash bottle with distilled water
- centrifuge
- blue litmus paper

- silver nitrate solution, 0.1 *M* AgNO$_3$
- dilute ammonium hydroxide, 6 *M* NH$_4$OH
- dilute nitric acid, 6 *M* HNO$_3$
- barium nitrate solution, 0.1 *M* Ba(NO$_3$)$_2$

- known anion solution (I$^-$, Cl$^-$, and SO$_4^{2-}$ as 0.1 *M* NaI, NaCl, Na$_2$SO$_4$)

- unknown anion solutions (I$^-$, Cl$^-$, and/or SO$_4^{2-}$ as 0.1 *M* NaI, NaCl, Na$_2$SO$_4$)

PROCEDURE

General Directions: Clean three test tubes and a glass stirring rod with distilled water. Label the test tubes #1, #2, and #3. As a solution is analyzed, record the color of each precipitate in the Data Table.

A. Analysis of a Known Anion Solution

1. *Identification of I$^-$ in a Known Solution*

(a) Place 10 drops of the known solution in test tube #1. Add 20 drops of silver nitrate, AgNO$_3$, and mix with a glass stirring rod.

>   **Note:** A yellow precipitate, AgI, suggests I$^-$ is present.

(b) Centrifuge the precipitate. Pour the supernate into test tube #3 and save for Step 3.

(c) Add 10 drops of dilute ammonium hydroxide, NH$_4$OH, to test tube #1 and stir thoroughly with a glass rod. Centrifuge the precipitate. Decant the supernate into test tube #2 and save for Step 2.

>   **Note:** A yellow precipitate, AgI, confirms I$^-$ is present. (*If the precipitate is white, add 10 drops of water and stir with a glass rod.*)

2. *Identification of Cl$^-$ in a Known Solution*

Add dilute nitric acid, HNO$_3$, dropwise into test tube #2 until the solution tests acidic on blue litmus paper. Centrifuge the precipitate.

>   **Note:** A white precipitate, AgCl, confirms Cl$^-$ is present. (*If the precipitate is yellow, it contains AgI particles from test tube #1.*)

3. *Identification of SO_4^{2-} in a Known Solution*

Add 10 drops of barium nitrate, $Ba(NO_3)_2$, to the solution in test tube #3. Centrifuge the precipitate.

Note: A white precipitate, $BaSO_4$, confirms SO_4^{2-} is present. (*If the precipitate is yellow, it contains AgI particles from test tube #1.*)

B. Analysis of an Unknown Anion Solution

1. *Identification of I^- in an Unknown Solution*

(a) Place 10 drops of unknown solution in test tube #1. Add 20 drops of silver nitrate, $AgNO_3$, and stir with a glass rod.

Note: If there is no precipitate, I^- and Cl^- are absent. Go directly to step 3.

(b) Centrifuge the precipitate. Pour the supernate into test tube #3, and save for Step 3.

(c) Add 10 drops of dilute ammonium hydroxide, NH_4OH, to test tube #1, and stir thoroughly with a glass rod. Centrifuge the precipitate. Decant the supernate into test tube #2, and save for Step 2.

Note: If there is no precipitate, I^- is absent. Go directly to Step 2.

2. *Identification of Cl^- in an Unknown Solution*

Add dilute nitric acid, HNO_3, dropwise to test tube #2 until the solution tests acidic on blue litmus paper. Centrifuge the precipitate.

Note: If there is no precipitate, Cl^- is absent. Go directly to Step 3.

3. *Identification of SO_4^{2-} in an Unknown Solution*

Add 10 drops of barium nitrate, $Ba(NO_3)_2$, to the solution in test tube #3. Centrifuge the precipitate.

Note: If there is no precipitate, SO_4^{2-} is absent.

4. Based on the observations in steps 1–3, identify the anion(s) present in the unknown solution.

PRELABORATORY ASSIGNMENT*

1. In your own words, define the following terms:

    anion

    aqueous solution

    centrifuge

    decant

    precipitate (ppt)

    qualitative analysis

    supernate

2. Why is it necessary to use distilled water throughout the experiment?

3. What color is the precipitate in test tube #1? in #2? in #3?

4. How is litmus paper used to test for an acidic solution?

5. What precautions should be taken while performing the experiment?

6. An unknown solution is analyzed for iodide, chloride, and sulfate ions.

    *   The unknown solution plus aqueous $AgNO_3$ gives a yellow precipitate.

    *   The supernate is poured into test tube #3.

    *   The yellow precipitate does not dissolve completely in aqueous NH_4OH.

    *   The supernate is decanted into test tube #2.

    *   Test tube #2 plus aqueous HNO_3 produces a white precipitate.

    *   Test tube #3 plus aqueous $Ba(NO_3)_2$ yields a white precipitate.

    Refer to Figure 3 and determine which of the following anions is (are) present in the unknown solution: I^-, Cl^-, and SO_4^{2-}.

---

*Answers at the end of the experiment.

NAME _____

DATE _____   SECTION _____

DATA TABLE

A. Analysis of a Known Anion Solution

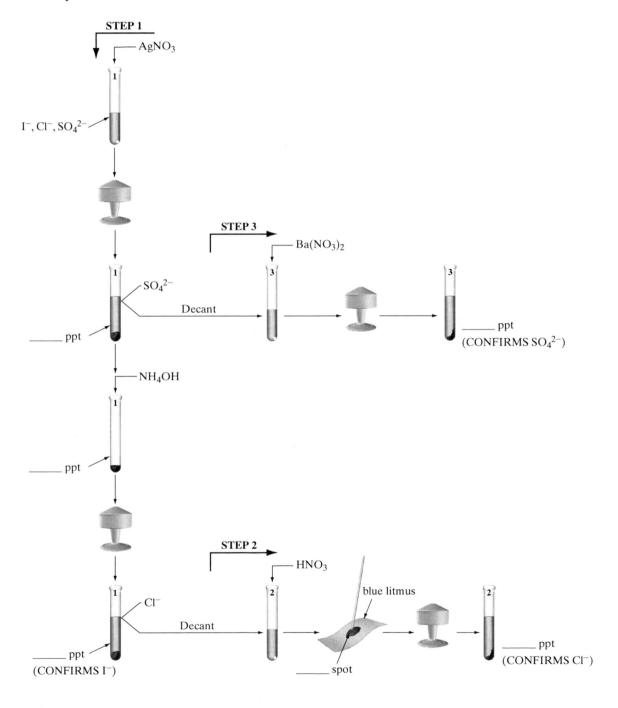

STEP 1

AgNO$_3$

I^-, Cl^-, SO_4^{2-}

STEP 3

Ba(NO$_3$)$_2$

SO$_4^{2-}$

Decant

_____ ppt

_____ ppt
(CONFIRMS SO$_4^{2-}$)

NH$_4$OH

_____ ppt

STEP 2

HNO$_3$

blue litmus

Cl$^-$

Decant

_____ ppt
(CONFIRMS I$^-$)

_____ spot

_____ ppt
(CONFIRMS Cl$^-$)

B. Analysis of an Unknown Anion Solution   **UNKNOWN #**_____

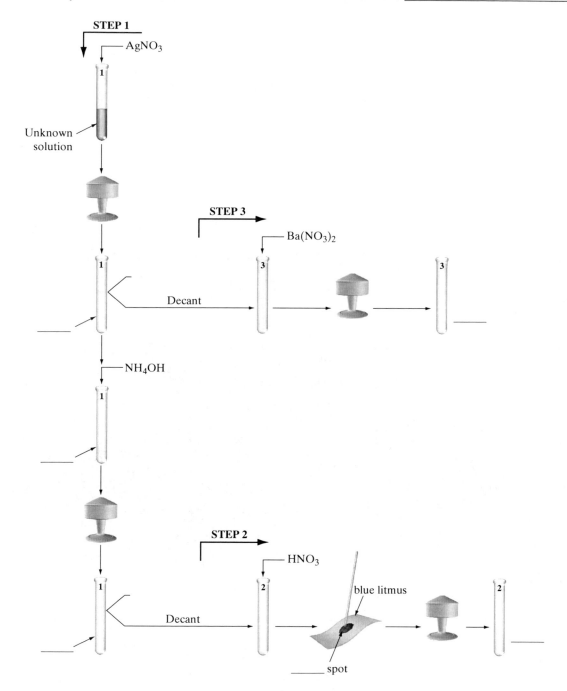

Answers to
Prelaboratory Assignment

IDENTIFYING ANIONS IN SOLUTION

1. See the Glossary.

2. Tap water contains many ions, some of which can interfere with the results of the analysis.

3. The AgI precipitate in test tube #1 confirms I^- should be yellow. (If the precipitate is white, add 10 drops of water and stir.) The AgCl precipitate in test tube #2 that confirms Cl^- and the $BaSO_4$ precipitate in test tube #3 that confirms SO_4^{2-}, should both be white. (If the precipitate in test tube #2 or #3 is yellow, there is AgI contamination from test tube #1.)

4. Place a thin glass stirring rod in the test solution, and touch it to blue litmus paper. If the paper turns red, the solution is acidic.

5. • Avoid contact with HNO_3 and NH_4OH. If contacted, wash the area immediately with water. Silver nitrate, $AgNO_3$, will temporarily stain your skin.

   • Balance the centrifuge before operating.

6. I^-, Cl^-, and SO_4^{2-} are all confirmed.

Experiment 6

Experiment 6

Empirical Formulas of Compounds

- To determine the empirical formula for magnesium oxide.
- To determine the empirical formula for copper sulfide.
- To gain practical experience in developing techniques using a crucible.

DISCUSSION

During the late 1700s, chemists experimented with elements to see how they reacted to form compounds. In particular, they were interested in the reactions of metals as they combined with oxygen gas in the air. By measuring the mass of a metal before reaction and the mass of the metal oxide after reaction, chemists were able to determine the formulas of metal oxide compounds.

The simplest whole number ratio of atoms in a compound is referred to as the **empirical formula**. Originally, an element was placed in a particular group in the periodic table based on the empirical formula of its oxide. For example, magnesium, calcium, strontium, and barium were placed in Group IIA/2 because they react with oxygen to give similar empirical formulas; that is, MgO, CaO, SrO, and BaO. Moreover, the empirical formulas of their chlorides are also similar; that is, $MgCl_2$, $CaCl_2$, $SrCl_2$, and $BaCl_2$.

Since transition metals can combine with nonmetals in different ratios, we cannot always predict the empirical formulas of their compounds. For example, iron can combine with oxygen to form either iron(II) oxide, FeO, or iron(III) oxide, Fe_2O_3. The following example exercises illustrate the calculation of empirical formulas.

Example Exercise 1 • Determining an Empirical Formula

A 0.279-g sample of iron is heated and allowed to react with oxygen from the air. If the product has a mass of 0.400 g, what is the empirical formula of the iron oxide?

Solution: The empirical formula is experimentally determined from the moles of each reactant. The moles of iron are calculated as follows.

$$0.279 \text{ g Fe} \times \frac{1 \text{ mol Fe}}{55.85 \text{ g Fe}} = 0.00500 \text{ mol Fe}$$

The mass of oxygen that reacted is 0.400 g product – 0.279 g iron = 0.121 g. We can calculate the moles of oxygen as follows.

$$0.121 \text{ g O} \times \frac{1 \text{ mol O}}{16.00 \text{ g O}} = 0.00756 \text{ mol O}$$

The mole ratio of the elements in iron oxide is $Fe_{0.00500}O_{0.00756}$, and we can divide by 0.00500 to find the simplest whole number ratio.

$$Fe\frac{0.00500}{0.00500} O\frac{0.00756}{0.00500} = Fe_{1.00}O_{1.51}$$

If we double the mole ratio, we obtain $Fe_2O_{3.02}$. We can explain the slight deviation from a whole number by experimental error. The empirical formula is Fe_2O_3, and we name the compound iron(III) oxide, or ferric oxide.

Example Exercise 2 • Determining an Empirical Formula

A 0.331-g sample of iron is placed in a crucible and covered with powdered sulfur. The crucible is heated until all the excess sulfur is driven off. If the product weighs 0.522 g, what is the empirical formula of the iron sulfide?

Solution: First, we can calculate the moles of iron in the product.

$$0.331 \text{ g Fe} \times \frac{1 \text{ mol Fe}}{55.85 \text{ g Fe}} = 0.00592 \text{ mol Fe}$$

The mass of sulfur that reacted is 0.522 g product – 0.331 g iron = 0.191 g. Second, we can calculate the moles of sulfur as follows.

$$0.191 \text{ g S} \times \frac{1 \text{ mol S}}{32.07 \text{ g S}} = 0.00596 \text{ mol S}$$

The mole ratio of the elements in iron sulfide is $Fe_{0.00592}S_{0.00596}$, and we divide by 0.00592 to find the simplest whole number ratio.

$$Fe\frac{0.00592}{0.00592} S\frac{0.00596}{0.00592} = Fe_{1.00}S_{1.01}$$

We explain the slight deviation from whole numbers by experimental error. The empirical formula for the product is FeS, and we name the compound iron(II) sulfide, or ferrous sulfide.

In this experiment, you will ignite magnesium ribbon in a crucible and convert the metal to an oxide product. The second part of the experiment involves the conversion of copper to copper sulfide. Since copper can form either copper(I) sulfide or copper(II) sulfide, the empirical formula is unknown and cannot be predicted. Figure 1 illustrates the experimental equipment.

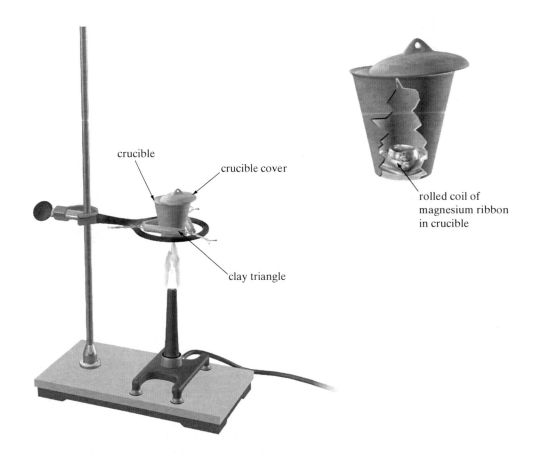

crucible

crucible cover

rolled coil of
magnesium ribbon
in crucible

clay triangle

Figure 1 Empirical Formula Apparatus A crucible and cover are placed
in a clay triangle on a ring stand, and heated until red hot.

EQUIPMENT and CHEMICALS

- clay triangle
- crucible tongs
- crucible and cover

- magnesium, Mg ribbon
- copper, #18 gauge Cu wire
- sulfur, S powder

PROCEDURE

A. Empirical Formula of Magnesium Oxide

1. Support a crucible and cover with a clay triangle, and place on a ring stand. Fire the crucible and cover to red heat using the tip of the flame from a laboratory burner.

2. Turn off the burner, and allow the crucible and cover to cool for 10 minutes. Weigh the crucible, and cover on a balance.

3. Cut a 25-cm strip of magnesium ribbon, and roll the metal into a flat coil. Place the coil of magnesium in the crucible so that it lies flat against the bottom. Reweigh the crucible, cover, and magnesium metal.

4. Return the crucible to the clay triangle. With the cover off, fire the crucible to red heat. When the magnesium sparks and begins to smoke, immediately remove the burner and place the cover on the crucible using crucible tongs.

    Note: Safety goggles should be worn when heating the magnesium in the crucible.

5. After the smoke has ceased, continue to heat the crucible and cover until the metal is completely converted to a gray-white residue. The progress of the reaction can be checked periodically by removing the burner and raising the cover with the crucible tongs.

6. When the metal no longer sparks, turn off the burner and allow the crucible to cool for 10 minutes. Using a dropper pipet, add drops of distilled water until no fizzing is observed from the gray-white residue.

    Note: Some of the magnesium reacts with nitrogen in the air to form magnesium nitride. Adding water decomposes the magnesium nitride and releases ammonia gas.

7. Cover the crucible, and heat for 5 minutes. Turn off the burner, and allow the crucible to cool for 10 minutes. Weigh the crucible and cover containing the magnesium oxide.

8. Clean the crucible, and repeat the procedure.

9. Calculate the empirical formula for each trial.

B. Empirical Formula of Copper Sulfide

   Caution: This procedure requires a vented fume hood, as burning sulfur produces pungent sulfur dioxide gas.

1. Support a crucible and cover with a clay triangle and place on a ring stand. Fire the crucible and cover to red heat.

2. Remove the heat, and allow the crucible and cover to cool for 10 minutes. Weigh the crucible and cover.

3. Cut a 25-cm length of copper wire, and roll the wire into a coil. Place the wire in the bottom of the crucible, and reweigh the crucible, cover, and copper wire.

4. Cover the copper wire completely with powdered sulfur. Place the cover on the crucible, and gradually heat to red heat under a fume hood. Continue to heat for several minutes after the last trace of burning sulfur disappears. Hold the burner in your hand and continue to heat the entire outside surface of the crucible and cover.

5. Allow the crucible and contents to cool for 10 minutes. Weigh the crucible and cover containing the copper sulfide.

6. Clean the crucible, and repeat the procedure.

7. Calculate the empirical formula for each trial.

PRELABORATORY ASSIGNMENT*

1. In your own words, define the following terms:

    empirical formula

    firing to red heat

    heating to constant weight

    molecular formula

    weighing by difference

2. Why are the empty crucible and cover fired to red heat?

3. How critical are the suggested times for heating and cooling?

4. Why is distilled water added to the crucible after igniting the magnesium metal?

---

*Answers at the end of the experiment.

5. How can you tell when the magnesium metal has reacted completely?

6. How can you tell when the copper wire has reacted completely and the excess sulfur has burned off?

7. A 0.250-g sample of calcium metal is heated in a 38.500-g crucible to form calcium oxide. If the crucible and product weigh 38.850 g, what is the empirical formula of calcium oxide?

8. What are the major sources of error in this experiment?

9. What safety precautions must be observed in this experiment?

NAME _____

DATE _____   SECTION _____

DATA TABLE

A. Empirical Formula of Magnesium Oxide

mass of crucible and cover + magnesium metal *(before heating)*	_____ g	_____ g
mass of crucible and cover	_____ g	_____ g
mass of magnesium metal	_____ g	_____ g
mass of crucible and cover + magnesium oxide *(after heating)*	_____ g	_____ g
mass of combined oxygen *(after heating – before heating)*	_____ g	_____ g

Show the calculation of the empirical formula for trial 1 (see Example Exercise 1).

Empirical formula of magnesium oxide   _____   _____

B. Empirical Formula of Copper Sulfide

mass of crucible and cover + copper wire
(before heating) _____ g _____ g

mass of crucible and cover _____ g _____ g

mass of copper wire _____ g _____ g

mass of crucible and cover + copper sulfide
(after heating) _____ g _____ g

mass of crucible and cover + copper sulfide
(optional second heating) _____ g _____ g

mass of combined sulfur _____ g _____ g
(after heating – before heating)

Show the calculation of the empirical formula for trial 1 (see Example Exercise 2).

Empirical formula of copper sulfide _____ _____

NAME _____

DATE _____   SECTION _____

POSTLABORATORY ASSIGNMENT

1. A 0.750-g sample of tin metal reacts with 0.201 g of oxygen gas to form tin oxide. Calculate the empirical formula of the tin oxide.

   _____

2. A 0.565-g sample of cobalt metal reacts with excess sulfur to give 1.027 g of cobalt sulfide. Calculate the empirical formula of the product.

   _____

3. A 1.164-g sample of iron filings reacts with chlorine gas to give 3.384 g of iron chloride. Calculate the empirical formula of the product?

   _____

4. A 0.626-g sample of copper oxide was reduced to 0.500 g of copper metal by heating in a stream of hydrogen gas. Calculate the empirical formula of the copper oxide.

   _____

5. A sample of phosphorus weighing 0.500 g was ignited to the oxide in a stream of oxygen gas. What is the empirical formula of phosphorus oxide if the product has a mass of 1.145 g? What is the molecular formula of phosphorus oxide if the molar mass is approximately 285 g/mol?

Empirical formula _____

Molecular formula _____

6. (optional) Ethylene glycol, the main ingredient in antifreeze, contains 38.7% carbon, 9.7% hydrogen, and 51.6% oxygen. Calculate the empirical and molecular formulas for ethylene glycol, given the molar mass is approximately 60 g/mol.

Empirical formula _____

Molecular formula _____

Answers to
Prelaboratory Assignment

EMPIRICAL FORMULAS OF COMPOUNDS

1. See the Glossary.

2. The empty crucible and cover are fired to red heat in order to burn off impurities in the crucible and to establish a constant weight.

3. The suggested periods for heating and cooling are general guidelines. More important, the metal should be heated long enough for complete conversion to the oxide. The crucible should be cooled sufficiently to avoid a buoyancy error at the balance.

4. Igniting magnesium in air produces magnesium nitride in addition to the magnesium oxide. Adding distilled water to the crucible contents decomposes magnesium nitride and releases ammonia gas. (The crucible contents fizz, and the odor of ammonia gas may be noticeable). Reheating the crucible and contents converts magnesium hydroxide to magnesium oxide.

5. If the magnesium metal has reacted completely, there will be no small sparks observed when the crucible cover is lifted.

6. We will assume that the copper wire has reacted completely when there are no longer any traces of yellow (or yellow-brown) sulfur in the crucible. If there is any doubt, heat the crucible to constant weight.

7. $Ca_{0.00624}O_{0.00625} = CaO$

8. • A hot crucible on the balance causes a buoyancy effect, and mass readings will be low.

- Smoke from the crucible indicates loss of magnesium oxide, and mass readings will be low.

- Sulfur has a tendency to "creep" out of the crucible during the firing. This excess sulfur must be heated and driven off as a gas, or the mass readings will be high.

9. • Before firing to red heat, set the crucible on the lab bench and strike sharply with a pencil. A crucible with a hairline crack gives a dull ring.

- A crucible that glows red has a temperature near 1100°C. Below this temperature, a crucible may not glow red, but it can cause a painful burn. Handle the crucible cover with tongs.

- The ignition of magnesium is strongly exothermic and frequently cracks crucibles. A few porcelain chips in the bottom of the crucible under the magnesium minimizes this problem.

- Heating copper and sulfur together produces toxic sulfur dioxide gas. Avoid breathing the gas, and vent the reaction under a fume hood.

- Wear goggle eye protection, especially when lifting the crucible cover to check the progress of the reaction.

Experiment 7

Experiment 7

Decomposing Baking Soda

OBJECTIVES

- To determine the percent yield of sodium carbonate from a decomposition reaction.
- To determine the percentage of sodium hydrogen carbonate in an unknown mixture.
- To gain proficiency in decomposing a compound and collecting a gas over water.

DISCUSSION

When baking soda is heated, sodium hydrogen carbonate, $NaHCO_3$, decomposes into solid sodium carbonate, while releasing steam and carbon dioxide gas. The equation for the reaction is

$$2\ NaHCO_3(s) \xrightarrow{\Delta} Na_2CO_3(s) + H_2O(g) + CO_2(g)$$

Notice that the reaction releases H_2O and CO_2 as gases but Na_2CO_3 remains a solid. If we weigh the mass of solid Na_2CO_3 produced in an experiment, the mass is referred to as the **actual yield**. Conversely, if we calculate the mass of Na_2CO_3 according to the balanced chemical equation, the mass is referred to as the **theoretical yield**.

The **percent yield** from the reaction is found by comparing the actual yield of Na_2CO_3 to the theoretical yield (all times 100). While some experimental errors lead to high results, other errors may give low results. Thus, the percent yield can be greater than—or less than—100%.

From *Prentice Hall Laboratory Manual for Introductory Chemistry,* Third Edition, Charles H. Corwin. Copyright © 2001 by Prentice Hall, Inc., a Pearson Education company. All rights reserved.

Percent Yield of Sodium Carbonate from Baking Soda

Example Exercise 1 • % Yield of Na2CO₃ from Baking Soda

A 1.654 g sample of baking soda, $NaHCO_3$, decomposes to produce 1.028 g of solid sodium carbonate. Calculate the theoretical yield and percent yield of Na_2CO_3.

Solution: According to the balanced equation, 2 mol $NaHCO_3$ (84.01 g/mol) produce 1 mol Na_2CO_3 (105.99 g/mol). We can find the theoretical yield as follows:

$$1.654 \text{ g NaHCO}_3 \times \frac{1 \text{ mol NaHCO}_3}{84.01 \text{ g NaHCO}_3} \times \frac{1 \text{ mol Na}_2\text{CO}_3}{2 \text{ mol NaHCO}_3} \times \frac{105.99 \text{ g Na}_2\text{CO}_3}{1 \text{ mol Na}_2\text{CO}_3}$$
$$= 1.043 \text{ g Na}_2\text{CO}_3$$

Since the actual yield of Na_2CO_3 is 1.028 g, the percent yield is

$$\frac{\text{actual yield}}{\text{theoretical yield}} \times 100 = \% \text{ yield}$$

$$\frac{1.028 \text{ g}}{1.043 \text{ g}} \times 100 = 98.56\%$$

Percentage of Sodium Hydrogen Carbonate in an Unknown Mixture

An unknown mixture containing baking soda is decomposed using heat. The following example exercise illustrates the calculation for the percentage of baking soda in the mixture.

Example Exercise 2 • % NaHCO₃ in an Unknown Mixture

A 1.675 g unknown mixture containing baking soda is decomposed with heat. If the mass loss is 0.318 g, what is the percentage of baking soda, $NaHCO_3$, in the unknown mixture?

Solution: In this example, the mass loss corresponds to both the mass of water vapor and carbon dioxide gas. To simplify the calculation, we will combine $H_2O + CO_2$ into H_2CO_3 (62.03 g/mol) and rewrite the chemical equation.

$$2 \text{ NaHCO}_3(s) \xrightarrow{\Delta} \text{Na}_2\text{CO}_3(s) + \text{H}_2\text{CO}_3(g)$$

We can relate the H_2CO_3 mass loss to the mass of $NaHCO_3$ as follows:

$$0.318 \text{ g H}_2\text{CO}_3 \times \frac{1 \text{ mol H}_2\text{CO}_3}{62.03 \text{ g H}_2\text{CO}_3} \times \frac{2 \text{ mol NaHCO}_3}{1 \text{ mol H}_2\text{CO}_3} \times \frac{84.01 \text{ g NaHCO}_3}{1 \text{ mol NaHCO}_3}$$
$$= 0.861 \text{ g NaHCO}_3$$

If the sample mixture has a mass of 1.675 g, the percentage of $NaHCO_3$ is

$$\frac{\text{mass NaHCO}_3}{\text{mass sample}} \times 100 = \% \text{ NaHCO}_3$$

$$\frac{0.861 \text{ g}}{1.675 \text{ g}} \times 100 = 51.4\%$$

Figure 1 shows the experimental apparatus for decomposing baking soda, as well as the unknown baking soda mixture. As the baking soda decomposes, carbon dioxide gas is produced. The carbon dioxide gas displaces water from the Florence flask into a beaker. When the decomposition is complete, no more carbon dioxide gas is released and the water level in the beaker remains constant.

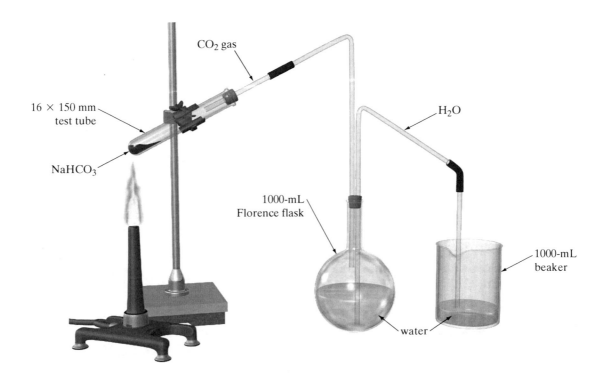

CO$_2$ gas

16 × 150 mm test tube

NaHCO$_3$

1000-mL Florence flask

H$_2$O

1000-mL beaker

water

Figure 1 Apparatus for Decomposition When the water level in the beaker remains constant, the decomposition of NaHCO$_3$ is complete.

EQUIPMENT and CHEMICALS

- gas collection apparatus (see Figure 1)
- 16 × 150 mm test tube
- 1000-mL Florence flask
- 1000-mL beaker

- sodium hydrogen carbonate, baking soda, solid NaHCO$_3$
- unknown baking soda mixture, 50–90% NaHCO$_3$

PROCEDURE

A. Percent Yield of Na_2CO_3 from Baking Soda

1. Weigh a 16×150 mm *dry* test tube on the balance, and record the mass. Add 1–2 g of baking soda, $NaHCO_3$, and reweigh accurately.

2. Set up the apparatus as shown in Figure 1. Fill the Florence flask to the neck with tap water, and insert the gas collection apparatus. Insert the small rubber stopper into the test tube as shown.

3. Begin heating the test tube gently. Observe the water being displaced into the beaker as carbon dioxide gas is produced. As the water level in the beaker increases, continue to heat the test tube with a gentle flame. After the water level remains constant for a couple of minutes, discontinue heating and allow the test tube to cool for 10 minutes.

    Note: The decomposition of baking soda produces steam that may collect in the test tube. Any moisture in the test tube leads to serious weighing errors. If there appears to be moisture in the test tube, remove the utility clamp from the ring stand and carefully heat the open test tube over a low flame until no trace of moisture remains. Allow the test tube to cool for 10 minutes before weighing.

    Note: Avoid heating the test tube to red heat, as the glass will tend to crack and break when moisture is present.

4. Weigh the test tube containing the sodium carbonate residue. The mass of Na_2CO_3 is found by subtracting the mass of the test tube from the test tube and residue.

5. Calculate the theoretical yield of sodium carbonate, Na_2CO_3, from the mass of pure baking soda that was heated. Find the percent yield of sodium carbonate.

B. Percentage of $NaHCO_3$ in an Unknown Mixture

1. Obtain an unknown sample containing baking soda. Record the unknown number in the Data Table.

2. Repeat steps 1–5 as in Procedure A, substituting the unknown mixture for the pure baking soda.

3. Calculate the mass of baking soda, $NaHCO_3$, in the unknown sample from the mass loss. Find the percentage of baking soda in the unknown mixture.

PRELABORATORY ASSIGNMENT*

1. In your own words, define the following terms:

    actual yield

    percent yield

    stoichiometry

    theoretical yield

    weighing by difference

2. How can you tell when the baking soda sample is completely decomposed?

3. Is it possible to have a percent yield of sodium carbonate that is greater than 100%?

4. A 1.500-g sample of baking soda, $NaHCO_3$, decomposes with heat to give 0.955 g of sodium carbonate. What is the percent yield of sodium carbonate?

---

*Answers at the end of the experiment.

5. A 2.000-g mixture containing baking soda is decomposed with heat. If the mass loss is 0.405 g, what is the percentage of baking soda, $NaHCO_3$, in the unknown mixture?

6. What are the primary sources of error in this experiment?

7. What safety precautions must be observed in this experiment?

Decomposing Baking Soda

NAME _____

DATE _____   SECTION _____

DATA TABLE

A. Percent Yield of Na_2CO_3 from Baking Soda

mass of test tube + $NaHCO_3$ *(before heating)*	_____ g	_____ g
mass of test tube	_____ g	_____ g
mass of $NaHCO_3$	_____ g	_____ g
mass of test tube + Na_2CO_3 *(after heating)*	_____ g	_____ g
mass of Na_2CO_3	_____ g	_____ g

Show the calculation for theoretical yield of Na_2CO_3 for trial 1 (see Example Exercise 1).

mass of Na_2CO_3 *(theoretical yield)*	_____ g	_____ g

Show the calculation for percent yield of Na_2CO_3 for trial 1 (see Example Exercise 1).

Percent Yield of Na_2CO_3	_____ %	_____ %
Average Percent Yield		_____ %

83

B. Percentage of $NaHCO_3$ in an Unknown Mixture   **UNKNOWN #**_____

mass of test tube + unknown mixture   _____ g   _____ g
(before heating)

mass of test tube   _____ g   _____ g

mass of unknown mixture   _____ g   _____ g

mass of test tube + residue   _____ g   _____ g
(after heating)

mass of H_2CO_3 (H_2O + CO_2)   _____ g   _____ g
(before heating – after heating)

Show the calculation for the mass of $NaHCO_3$ in the unknown mixture for trial 1 (see Example
    Exercise 2).

mass of $NaHCO_3$ _____ g   _____ g

Show the calculation for the percentage of $NaHCO_3$ in the unknown mixture for trial 1 (see Example
    Exercise 2).

Percentage of $NaHCO_3$ _____ %   _____ %

Average percentage of $NaHCO_3$ _____ %

Answers to Prelaboratory Assignment

---

1. See the Glossary.

2. When all the baking soda is decomposed, carbon dioxide is no longer produced and the water level in the beaker remains constant. After the burner is shut off, the water level will actually decrease in the beaker as the gas is allowed to cool.

3. Yes, some errors can lead to high results, giving a percent yield greater than 100%.

4. (0.955 g/0.946 g) × 100% = 101%

5. (1.10 g/2.000 g) × 100% = 55.0%

6. • Heating the baking soda mixture insufficiently leads to high results.
   • Weighing the test tube containing traces of moisture from the decomposition of baking soda gives a heavy mass reading.
   • Weighing the test tube while warm causes a buoyancy effect and gives a light mass reading.

7. • Wear goggle eye protection, especially when heating substances in a test tube.
   • Avoid pinching off the rubber tubing leading from the test tube to the Florence flask.

Experiment 8

Experiment 8

Molecular Models and Chemical Bonds

OBJECTIVES

- To construct models of molecules with single, double, and triple bonds.
- To draw the structural formula for a molecule based on the molecular model.
- To draw the electron dot formula corresponding to the structural formula.
- To draw the structural and electron dot formulas for unknown molecular models.

DISCUSSION

The attraction between two atoms in a molecule is called a chemical bond. In a **covalent bond,** two nonmetal atoms are attracted to each other by sharing valence electrons. The **valence electrons** are the electrons farthest from the nucleus and occupy the highest *s* and *p* sublevels. The number of valence electrons is found from the periodic table. The group number of an element indicates the number of valence electrons. For example, fluorine is in Group VIIA/17 and has seven valence electrons (7 e^-).

Example Exercise 1 • Valence Electrons and the Periodic Table

Refer to the periodic table, and determine the number of valence electrons for the following elements: (a) H; (b) C; (c) N; (d) O; (e) Cl, Br, I.

Solution: (a) The element hydrogen is in Group IA/1. Since the group number is 1, hydrogen has one valence electron.

(b) Carbon is in Group IVA/14; thus, carbon has four valence electrons.

(c) Nitrogen is in Group VA/15; thus, nitrogen has five valence electrons. However, under ordinary conditions, only three of nitrogen's valence electrons are shared. The remaining two electrons do not usually bond and are referred to as nonbonding electrons.

(d) Oxygen is in Group VIA/16; thus, oxygen has six valence electrons.

(e) Chlorine, bromine, and iodine are in Group VIIA/17; thus, each of the halogens has seven valence electrons.

In this experiment, we will draw the **structural formula** and **electron dot formula** for molecules after building a model. A model is constructed from spherical balls and connectors, where each ball represents an atom and each connector a single bond. Since a **single bond** shares two electrons, each connector represents an electron pair.

A **double bond** shares two pairs of electrons. A molecular model is constructed using two connectors to represent the double bond. A **triple bond** shares three pairs of electrons. A molecular model is constructed using three connectors to represent the triple bond.

The following example exercises illustrate the structural formula and electron dot formula for molecular models having single, double, and triple bonds.

Example Exercise 2 • Structural and Electron Dot Formula for H$_2$O

The molecular model of water is sketched below. Draw (a) the structural formula, and (b) the electron dot formula corresponding to the model, and (c) verify the electron dot formula by checking the total number of electron dots against the sum of all valence electrons.

water, H$_2$O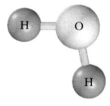

Solution: (a) Each connector represents a single bond; the structural formula is

H — O
|
H

(b) A dash in the structural formula indicates an electron pair, thus

H : O
:
H

Each hydrogen atom shares a maximum of two electrons. However, each oxygen requires an octet of electrons and in the above diagram shares only four. Therefore, we must add two more pairs of electrons to oxygen in order to complete the octet. The electron dot formula is

$$\text{H} : \overset{\displaystyle ..}{\underset{\displaystyle ..}{\text{O}}} :$$
$$\text{H}$$

(c) To verify the above formula, we will add up the valence electrons from each atom in the molecule. Recall that hydrogen is in Group IA/1 and oxygen is in Group VIA/6.

$$2\,\text{H}\,(2 \times 1\,e^-) = 2\,e^-$$
$$1\,\text{O}\,(1 \times 6\,e^-) = \underline{6\,e^-}$$
$$\text{sum of valence electrons} = 12\,e^-$$

There are eight dots used to draw the electron dot formula. Since this equals the number of valence electrons, the electron dot formula is correct.

Example Exercise 3 • Structural and Electron Dot Formula for CHCl₃

The molecular model of chloroform is sketched below. Draw (a) the structural formula and (b) the electron dot formula. Each atom (excluding H) should be surrounded by an octet of electrons. (c) Verify the electron dot formula by checking the total number of electron dots against the sum of all valence electrons.

chloroform, CHCl₃

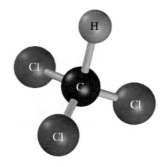

Solution: (a) Each stick represents a single bond, so the structural formula is

$$\text{H}$$
$$|$$
$$\text{Cl} - \text{C} - \text{Cl}$$
$$|$$
$$\text{Cl}$$

(b) Each dash in the structural formula indicates an electron pair; therefore,

$$\text{H}$$
$$\overset{\displaystyle ..}{}$$
$$\text{Cl} : \text{C} : \text{Cl}$$
$$\overset{\displaystyle ..}{}$$
$$\text{Cl}$$

Hydrogen and carbon are complete as shown; two electrons and eight electrons, respectively. However, each chlorine also requires an octet, which we will complete as follows:

$$
\begin{array}{c}
\text{H} \\
\overset{..}{} \\
:\overset{..}{\underset{..}{\text{Cl}}} : \text{C} : \overset{..}{\underset{..}{\text{Cl}}} : \\
\text{Cl}
\end{array}
$$

(c) To verify the above electron dot formula, we will find the sum of all valence electrons.

$$1\ \text{H} \,(1 \times 1\ e^-) = 1\ e^-$$
$$1\ \text{C} \,(1 \times 4\ e^-) = 4\ e^-$$
$$3\ \text{Cl} \,(3 \times 7\ e^-) = \underline{21\ e^-}$$
$$\text{sum of valence electrons} = 26\ e^-$$

There are 26 valence electrons, and 26 dots were used in the electron dot formula; thus, the formula is verified.

Example Exercise 4 • Structural and Electron Dot Formula for H$_2$CO

A molecular model of formaldehyde is sketched below. Draw the (a) structural formula and (b) electron dot formula. (c) Find the sum of all valence electrons to verify the electron dot formula.

formaldehyde, H$_2$CO

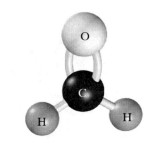

Solution: (a) Two connectors joining the carbon and oxygen atoms represent a double bond. The structural formula can be shown as

$$
\begin{array}{c}
\text{O} \\
\| \\
\text{H} - \text{C} - \text{H}
\end{array}
$$

(b) Each single bond contains one electron pair, and the double bond two electron pairs.

$$
\begin{array}{c}
\text{O} \\
\overset{..}{\underset{..}{}} \\
\text{H} : \text{C} : \text{H}
\end{array}
$$

Hydrogen shares two electrons and is stable. Carbon shares a total of eight electrons and satisfies the octet rule. Oxygen has only four of the eight electrons necessary to complete the octet. Therefore, we will add two unshared electron pairs.

$$\overset{\cdot\cdot}{\underset{\cdot\cdot}{:\text{O}}}$$
$$\text{H} : \text{C} : \text{H}$$

(c) We can verify the above electron dot formula as follows:

$$2\,\text{H}\,(2 \times 1\,\text{e}^-) = 2\,\text{e}^-$$
$$1\,\text{C}\,(1 \times 4\,\text{e}^-) = 4\,\text{e}^-$$
$$1\,\text{O}\,(1 \times 6\,\text{e}^-) = \underline{6\,\text{e}^-}$$
$$\text{sum of valence electrons} = 12\,\text{e}^-$$

The 12 valence electrons equal the 12 electron dots and verify the formula.

Example Exercise 5 • Structural and Electron Dot Formula for HCN

A molecular model of hydrogen cyanide is sketched below. Draw (a) the structural formula and (b) the electron dot formula. (c) Verify the electron dot formula.

hydrogen cyanide, HCN

Solution: (a) The three connectors linking the carbon and nitrogen represent a triple pair of electrons.

$$\text{H} - \text{C} \equiv \text{N}$$

(b) We can draw an electron dot formula after realizing the triple bond contains three electron pairs.

$$\text{H} : \text{C} ::: \text{N}$$

In the above formula, nitrogen shares only six electrons. Therefore, we must add one unshared electron pair.

$$\text{H} : \text{C} ::: \text{N}:$$

(c) Let's verify the preceding electron dot formula.

$$1\,\text{H}\,(1 \times 1\,\text{e}^-) = 1\,\text{e}^-$$
$$1\,\text{C}\,(1 \times 4\,\text{e}^-) = 4\,\text{e}^-$$
$$1\,\text{N}\,(1 \times 5\,\text{e}^-) = \underline{5\,\text{e}^-}$$
$$\text{sum of valence electrons} = 10\,\text{e}^-$$

The 10 valence electrons verify the 10 e⁻ dots.

EQUIPMENT and CHEMICALS

- molecular model kits

Directions for Using Molecular Models

When constructing a model, a hole in a ball represents a missing electron that is necessary to complete an octet. If two balls are joined by one connector, the connector represents a single bond composed of one electron pair. If two balls are joined by two connectors, the two connectors represent a double bond composed of two electron pairs. If two balls are joined by three connectors, the three connectors represent a triple bond composed of three electron pairs.

one rigid connector — single bond (one electron pair)

two flexible connectors — double bond (two electron pairs)

three flexible connectors — triple bond (three electron pairs)

A molecular model uses different color balls to represent hydrogen, carbon, oxygen, chlorine, bromine, iodine, and nitrogen atoms. The color code for each ball is as follows:

white ball — hydrogen (one hole)

black ball — carbon (four holes)

red ball — oxygen (two holes)

green ball — chlorine (one hole)

orange ball — bromine (one hole)

purple ball — iodine (one hole)

blue ball — nitrogen (three holes)

Note: If the blue nitrogen ball has more than three holes, use a small peg or tape to fill the additional hole(s). All the holes in each ball must have a connector for a model to be built correctly.

PROCEDURE

1. Construct models for each of the molecules listed on the next page. Sketch the molecular model in the Data Table, showing its three-dimensional structure.

2. Draw the structural formula corresponding to the molecular model.

3. Draw the electron dot formula corresponding to the structural formula. Complete the octet by surrounding each atom with 8 electrons (2 electrons for a hydrogen atom).

4. Verify each electron dot formula by summing the valence electrons for the molecule, using the periodic table. This sum should equal the total number of dots in the electron dot formula.

Molecular Models and Chemical Bonds

A. Molecular Models with Single Bonds

  (a) H_2 (b) Cl_2

  (c) Br_2 (d) I_2

  (e) HCl   (f) HBr

  (g) ICl   (h) CH_4

  (i) CH_2Cl_2 (j) HOCl

  (k) H_2O_2 (l) NH_3

  (m) N_2H_4 (n) NH_2OH

B. Molecular Models with Double Bonds

  (a) O_2 (b) C_2H_4

  (c) HONO   (d) HCOOH

  (e) C_2H_3Cl

C. Molecular Models with Triple Bonds

  (a) N_2 (b) C_2H_2

  (c) HOCN

D. Molecular Models with Two Double Bonds

  (a) CO_2 (b) C_3H_4

E. Unknown Molecular Models

The instructor will provide models of unknown molecules. Draw the structural formula for each unknown model and the electron dot formula corresponding to each structural formula.

PRELABORATORY ASSIGNMENT*

1. In your own words, define the following terms:

    covalent bond

    double bond

    electron dot formula

    octet rule

    single bond

    structural formula

    triple bond

    valence electrons

2. Refer to the periodic table in order to predict the number of valence electrons for each of the following elements: H, C, O, Cl, and N.

3. What do each of the following represent in the molecular model kit?

    (a) a white ball   (b) a black ball

    (c) a red ball   (d) a blue ball

    (e) one rigid connector   (f) two flexible connectors

4. Draw the structural formula and electron dot formula for each of the following:

    (a) IBr   (b) CH_3Cl

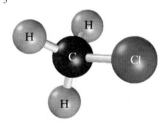

    (c) Cl_2CO

5. Perform a valence electron check on each of the examples in the preceding questions.

---

*Answers at the end of the experiment.

96

Answers to
Prelaboratory Assignment

MOLECULAR MODELS AND CHEMICAL BONDS

1. See the Glossary.

2. The number of valence electrons correspond to the group number of the element; thus,

   H = 1, C = 4, O = 6, Cl = 7, and N = 5.

3. (a) hydrogen atom   (b) carbon atom

   (c) oxygen atom   (d) nitrogen atom

   (e) single bond (2 e$^-$)   (f) double bond (4 e$^-$)

4. (a) I — Br

   (b)

   (c)

5. (a) $7\,e^- + 7\,e^- = 14\,e^-$ (b) $4\,e^- + 3(1\,e^-) + 7\,e^- = 14\,e^-$

   (c) $2(7\,e^-) + 4\,e^- + 6\,e^- = 24\,e^-$

Experiment 9

Experiment 9

Freezing Points and Melting Points

OBJECTIVES

- To gain proficiency in constructing a graph and plotting data points.
- To determine the freezing point of a compound from the graph of decreasing temperature versus time.
- To determine the melting points of a known and unknown compound.

DISCUSSION

A sample of matter can exist in the solid, liquid, or gaseous state. The **physical state** of a substance depends on the temperature and atmospheric pressure. For example, water can exist as solid ice at temperatures below 0°C and as gaseous steam above 100°C.

A **change of state** occurs when there is sufficient heat energy for individual molecules to overcome their attraction for each other. For example, when ice is converted to water, the water molecules in the ice crystal acquire enough energy to become free of each other and move around. Conversely, when water cools to ice, the water molecules lose energy and can no longer move about. Thus, a solid is composed of fixed particles and a liquid has mobile particles.

At the temperature where a liquid changes to a solid, two physical states are present simultaneously. This temperature is referred to as the **freezing point**. Conversely, if a solid changes to a liquid, it is called the **melting point**. Theoretically, the freezing and melting points of a substance occur at the same temperature.

In this experiment, we will melt paradichlorobenzene and then allow the liquid to cool to a solid. We will record the temperature/time relationship, plot the data, and graph a cooling curve. The temperature should remain constant as the liquid solidifies. Figure 1 shows a typical cooling curve.

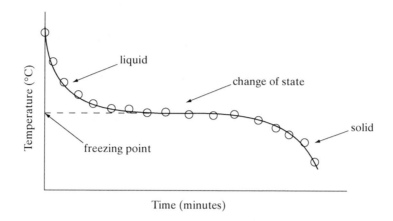

Figure 1 Cooling Curve As a liquid cools, it changes state from a liquid to a solid. The freezing point corresponds to the flat plateau portion of the curve.

As the compound cools, crystals begin to form. After a few minutes the crystals become a solid mass as the liquid changes to a solid. We will plot temperature on the vertical axis, which is called the **ordinate**. We will plot time on the horizontal axis, which is referred to as the **abscissa**. The freezing point of the compound is the temperature corresponding to the flat plateau. The apparatus for determining the cooling curve is shown in Figure 2.

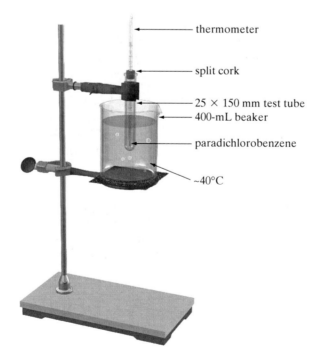

Figure 2 Change of State Apparatus The melted paradichlorobenzene is inside a test tube, which in turn, is placed in a beaker of water at ~40°C.

In the second procedure of this experiment a melting point is determined. A small sample of compound is rapidly heated until it is observed to liquefy. The temperature range over which the compound melts is recorded; for example, 65–75°C. A second trial is repeated for greater accuracy. The waterbath is heated rapidly to 60°C and then slowly until the compound melts. This second trial should produce an accurate melting point with a 1–2°C range; for example 69.5–71.0°C.

EQUIPMENT and CHEMICALS

- wire gauze
- mortar and pestle
- 110°C thermometer with split cork
- 400-mL beaker
- 25 × 150 mm test tube containing 20 g of paradichlorobenzene

- 50 cm of 6-mm glass tubing
- capillary tubes
- rubber bands
- biphenyl (diphenyl)
- melting point unknowns

PROCEDURE

A. Cooling Curve and Freezing Point

The instructor may wish to have students work in pairs. One student should set up the apparatus and record data while the other student heats the paradichlorobenzene and later observes temperature readings.

1. Set up the apparatus as shown in Figure 2. Add 300 mL of distilled water to the 400-mL beaker. Heat the water to 40°C, and shut off the burner.

2. Obtain a test tube containing paradichlorobenzene and immerse the test tube in a waterbath of boiling water. After the compound has melted, insert a thermometer into the test tube and continue heating until the liquid is well above 65°C.

   Note: It may be convenient for the instructor to provide a large, hot waterbath to heat the test tubes containing paradichlorobenzene.

3. Transfer the test tube and thermometer into the 400-mL beaker of water at 40°C. Support the test tube with a utility clamp, and hold the thermometer using a split cork as shown in Figure 2.

4. Begin recording thermometer readings when the temperature drops to 65.0°C. Continue recording the temperature (± 0.5°C) every 30 seconds for ten minutes.

5. Plot the temperature/time data on the graph paper provided. Circle each point, and draw a smooth cooling curve. Extend a dashed line from the flat portion of the curve to the vertical axis in order to determine the freezing point of the compound.

   Note: If the thermometer is frozen in solid paradichlorobenzene, **do not attempt to pull out the thermometer**. Return the test tube to the hot waterbath and allow the solid to melt; then remove the thermometer. Do not pour out the liquid paradichlorobenzene, as the compound is used for repeated trials.

B. Melting Point of an Unknown

1. Seal one end of a capillary tube with a burner flame. Let the tube cool, and then dab the open end into a small sample of biphenyl. Invert the capillary and lightly tap the sealed end to pack the sample. Repeat this process until a 5–mm sample is packed at the sealed end of the capillary.

   Note: If the biphenyl crystals are large, grind the crystals using a mortar and pestle. To pack the crystals, drop the sealed end of the capillary through a long piece of 6-mm glass tubing onto the lab bench.

2. Set up an apparatus as shown in Figure 3. Add 300 mL of distilled water into the 400-mL beaker. Attach the capillary at the end of the thermometer with a rubber band, and place in the beaker.

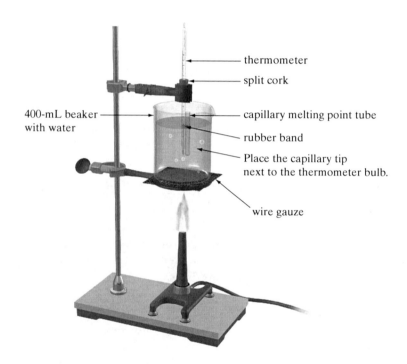

Figure 3 Melting Point Apparatus The melting point is recorded when the solid melts to a liquid and appears clear in the capillary tube.

3. Rapidly heat the water in the beaker until the biphenyl melts. Observe the approximate melting point (± 1°C), and record the range of temperature in the Data Table.

4. Prepare another capillary tube and heat rapidly until the temperature is within 10°C of the melting point. Then slowly continue to heat in order to determine the melting point accurately. Record the melting point range (± 0.5°C) from the first sign of melting until the compound has completely melted. The reference value is given in the Data Table for comparison.

5. Obtain an unknown compound, and record the number. Determine the melting point for the unknown as above.

1. In your own words, define the following terms:

   abscissa

   change of state

   freezing point

   melting point

   ordinate

   origin

   physical state

2. Why is distilled water used in a hot waterbath?

3. When the test tube with hot liquid paradichlorobenzene is placed in the beaker of water to cool, what is the initial temperature of the water in the beaker?

4. When the test tube with hot liquid paradichlorobenzene is placed in the beaker of water, what is the initial temperature of the paradichlorobenzene in the test tube?

5. When the test tube with hot liquid paradichlorobenzene is placed in the beaker of water, what is the initial *recorded* temperature reading?

6. The freezing point of paradichlorobenzene corresponds to which point on the cooling curve?

7. After the liquid paradichlorobenzene freezes, how is the thermometer removed from the frozen solid?

8. In determining a melting point of a compound, why are two trials performed?

---

*Answers at the end of the experiment.

9. While performing the first melting point trial, a compound begins to melt at 65°C and liquefies completely at 75°C. Report the approximate melting point.

10. While performing the second melting point trial, a compound begins to melt at 68.0°C and liquefies completely at 69.5°C. Report the precise melting point.

11. A solid compound in a capillary tube is placed in the waterbath and appears to liquefy before heating. Give two possible explanations of the problem.

12. What safety precautions must be observed in this experiment?

NAME _____

DATE _____   SECTION _____

DATA TABLE

A. Cooling Curve and Freezing Point

Temperature	Time	Observation
65.0°C	0:00	liquid
	0:30	
	1:00	
	1:30	
	2:00	
	2:30	
	3:00	
	3:30	
	4:00	
	4:30	
	5:00	
	5:30	
	6:00	
	6:30	
	7:00	
	7:30	
	8:00	
	8:30	
	9:00	
	9:30	
	10:00	

B. Melting Point of an Unknown

	Rapid Trial	Trial 2
Mp of biphenyl (69–71°C)	_____ °C	_____ °C
Mp of **UNKNOWN** #_____	_____ °C	_____ °C

A. Cooling Curve—Trial 2

Temperature	Time	Observation
65.0°C	0:00	liquid
	0:30	
	1:00	
	1:30	
	2:00	
	2:30	
	3:00	
	3:30	
	4:00	
	4:30	
	5:00	
	5:30	
	6:00	
	6:30	
	7:00	
	7:30	
	8:00	
	8:30	
	9:00	
	9:30	
	10:00	

Freezing Points and Melting Points

A. Cooling Curve—Trial 1   Freezing Point:_____°C

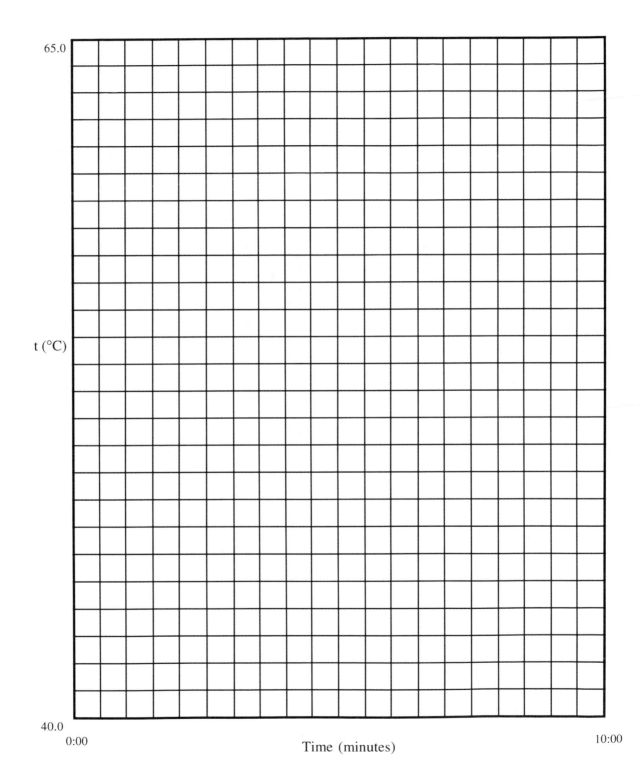

t (°C)

65.0

40.0

0:00   Time (minutes)   10:00

B. Cooling Curve—Trial 2   Freezing Point:_____°C

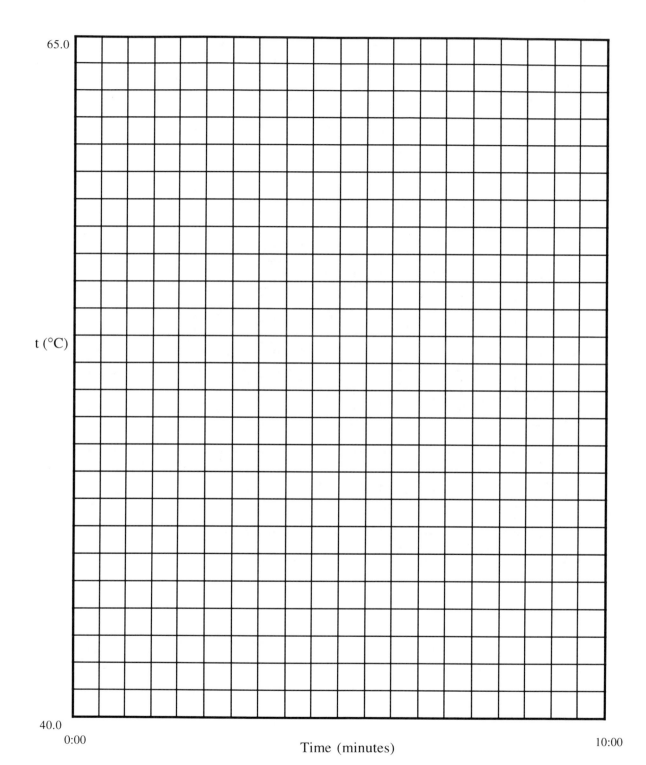

t (°C)

65.0

40.0

0:00   Time (minutes)   10:00

NAME _____

DATE _____   SECTION _____

POSTLABORATORY ASSIGNMENT

1. Methane, natural gas, freezes to a solid at −182°C. What is the freezing point on the Kelvin and Fahrenheit scales?

   _____

   _____

2. Sodium chloride, table salt, melts to a liquid at 801°C. What is the melting point on the Kelvin and Fahrenheit scales?

   _____

   _____

3. The following graph depicts a heating curve for acetic acid:

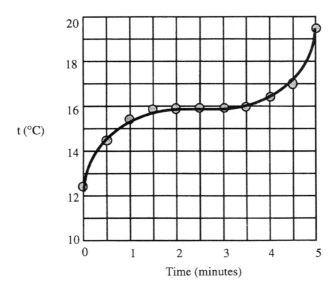

   From the graph, estimate the melting point of acetic acid ± 0.5°C.

   _____

4. Using the following data for the compound benzene, label the ordinate and abscissa axes and graph the cooling curve.

Temperature (°C)	Time (minutes)
10.0	0:00
7.5	0:30
6.5	1:00
6.0	1:30
5.5	2:00
5.5	2:30
5.5	3:00
5.5	3:30
5.5	4:00
5.0	4:30
4.0	5:00

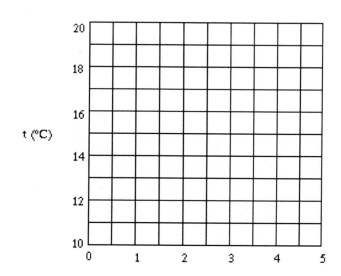

From the graph, estimate the freezing point of benzene ± 0.5°C.

_____

5. (optional) Using the *Handbook of Chemistry and Physics, Physical Constants of Organic Compounds,* find the melting points of the following compounds.

(a) acetic acid

_____

(b) benzene

_____

Answers to
Prelaboratory Assignment

---

1. See the Glossary.

2. Hot tap water can leave mineral deposits on glassware.

3. ~40°C

4. above 65°C

5. 65.0°C

6. The freezing point corresponds to the flat *plateau* portion of the curve. The freezing point is determined by extending a straight line from the plateau on the curve back to the vertical axis.

7. Place the test tube containing the solid paradichlorobenzene in hot water. After the compound melts, remove the thermometer and wipe off any residue with a paper towel.

8. Determining a melting point is time-consuming if the substance is heated 1°C per minute. Therefore, heat the water rapidly for the first trial, and determine an approximate melting point. In the second trial, heat the water rapidly to within a few degrees of the approximate melting point and then slowly (about 1°C per minute) to determine an accurate melting point.

9. 65–75°C

10. 68.0–69.5°C

11. If the compound appears to liquefy, the problem may be that
    (1) The temperature of the waterbath is higher than the melting point of the compound.
    (2) The capillary may not be sealed completely, and water may be leaking into the tube.

12. • Wear goggle eye protection, especially when using the laboratory burner.
    • Do not heat the test tube directly because paradichlorobenzene is flammable.
    • Do not pour out the liquid paradichlorobenzene, as it is used for repeated trials.
    • Handle the thermometer carefully, and do not attempt to remove a thermometer frozen in solid paradichlorobenzene. (Report a broken thermometer immediately to the Instructor.

Experiment 10

Experiment 10

Analysis of Vinegar

OBJECTIVES

- To standardize a sodium hydroxide solution with potassium hydrogen phthalate.
- To determine the molar concentration and mass/mass percent concentration of acetic acid in an unknown vinegar solution.
- To gain proficiency in the laboratory technique of titration.

DISCUSSION

In this experiment, we will neutralize an acidic solution of vinegar using a basic solution of sodium hydroxide. We will determine the amount of sodium hydroxide necessary by performing a **titration** using a buret. When the acid is completely neutralized by the base, the titration stops. This is called the **endpoint** and is signaled when an **indicator** changes color. The indicator in this experiment is phenolphthalein, which is colorless in acid and pink in base. At the endpoint in the titration, a single drop of base is sufficient to bring about a color change from colorless to pink. Figure 1 illustrates a typical titration.

We will begin the experiment by diluting 6 M NaOH with water. Since the dilution of NaOH provides only an approximate concentration, it is necessary to determine the concentration precisely by **standardization**. To standardize NaOH, we will weigh crystals of potassium hydrogen phthalate, $KHC_8H_4O_4$ (abbreviated KHP). After dissolving the KHP crystals in water, we will titrate the acid solution with NaOH according to the following equation.

$$KHP(aq) + NaOH(aq) \rightarrow KNaP(aq) + H_2O(l)$$

From *Prentice Hall Laboratory Manual for Introductory Chemistry,* Third Edition, Charles H. Corwin. Copyright © 2001 by Prentice Hall, Inc., a Pearson Education company. All rights reserved.

Example Exercise 1 • Molar Concentration of Standard NaOH

A 0.905 g sample of KHP (204.23 g/mol) is dissolved in water and titrated with 19.90 mL of NaOH solution to a phenolphthalein endpoint. Find the molarity of the NaOH solution.

Solution: Referring to the preceding equation for the reaction and applying the rules of stoichiometry, we have

$$0.905 \; \text{g KHP} \times \frac{1 \; \text{mol KHP}}{204.23 \; \text{g KHP}} \times \frac{1 \; \text{mol NaOH}}{1 \; \text{mol KHP}} = 0.00443 \; \text{mol NaOH}$$

The molarity of the NaOH is found as follows:

$$\frac{0.00443 \; \text{mol NaOH}}{19.90 \; \text{mL solution}} \times \frac{1000 \; \text{mL}}{1 \; \text{L}} = \frac{0.223 \; \text{mol NaOH}}{1 \; \text{L solution}} = 0.223 \; \text{M NaOH}$$

In this example, the concentration of the standard NaOH solution is 0.223 *M*.

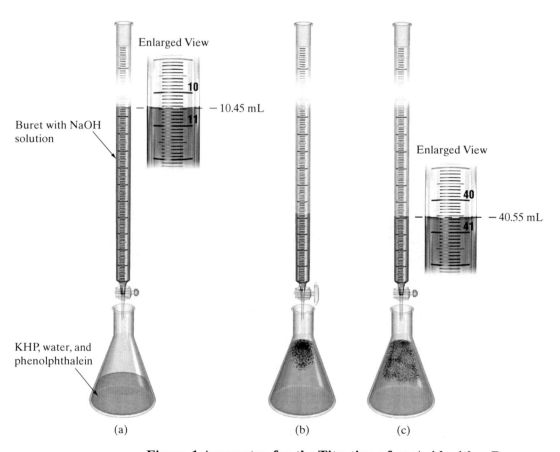

Enlarged View

— 10.45 mL

Buret with NaOH solution

Enlarged View

— 40.55 mL

KHP, water, and phenolphthalein

(a)   (b)   (c)

Figure 1 Apparatus for the Titration of an Acid with a Base

(a) Read the initial volume of NaOH in the buret (10.45 mL). (b) A flash of pink indicates an approaching endpoint. (c) A permanent pink color signals the final endpoint. Read the final volume of NaOH in the buret (40.55 mL). The volume of NaOH used for the titration is 40.55 mL – 10.45 mL = 30.10 mL.

After standardizing the sodium hydroxide solution, we can determine the concentration of acetic acid in an unknown vinegar solution. A sample of vinegar will be titrated with NaOH to a phenolphthalein endpoint. The equation for the reaction is

$$HC_2H_3O_2(aq) + NaOH(aq) \rightarrow NaC_2H_3O_2(aq) + H_2O(l)$$

The following example exercise illustrates the calculation for the percentage of acetic acid in an unknown vinegar sample.

Example Exercise 2 • Percentage of Acetic Acid in Vinegar

The titration of a 10.0-mL vinegar sample requires 29.05 mL of standard 0.223 M NaOH. Calculate the (a) molarity and (b) mass/mass percent concentration of acetic acid.

Solution: We can calculate the moles of acetic acid from the moles of NaOH solution:

$$29.05 \text{ mL solution} \times \frac{0.223 \text{ mol NaOH}}{1000 \text{ mL solution}} \times \frac{1 \text{ mol } HC_2H_3O_2}{1 \text{ mol NaOH}} = 0.00648 \text{ mol } HC_2H_3O_2$$

(a) The molar concentration of $HC_2H_3O_2$ is

$$\frac{0.00648 \text{ mol } HC_2H_3O_2}{10.0 \text{ mL solution}} \times \frac{1000 \text{ mL}}{1 \text{ L}} = \frac{0.648 \text{ mol } HC_2H_3O_2}{1 \text{ L solution}}$$
$$= 0.648 \text{ M } HC_2H_3O_2$$

(b) To calculate the m/m % concentration, we must know the density of the vinegar (1.01 g/mL) and the molar mass of acetic acid (60.06 g/mol).

$$\frac{0.648 \text{ mol } HC_2H_3O_2}{1000 \text{ mL solution}} \times \frac{60.06 \text{ g } HC_2H_3O_2}{1 \text{ mol } HC_2H_3O_2} \times \frac{1 \text{ mL solution}}{1.01 \text{ g solution}} \times 100$$
$$= 3.85\% \; HC_2H_3O_2$$

EQUIPMENT and CHEMICALS

- graduated cylinder
- 1000-mL Florence flask w/stopper
- 125-mL Erlenmeyer flasks (3)
- buret stand (or ring stand)
- buret clamp (or utility clamp)
- small, plastic funnel (optional)
- 50-mL buret
- 10-mL pipet and pipet bulb
- 100-mL beaker
- 150-mL beaker
- wash bottle with distilled water

- dilute sodium hydroxide, 6 M NaOH
- potassium hydrogen phthalate, solid $KHC_8H_4O_4$ (KHP)
- phenolphthalein indicator
- unknown vinegar solution, 3.00–5.00% $HC_2H_3O_2$

PROCEDURE

A. Preparation of Standard Sodium Hydroxide Solution

1. Half fill a 1000-mL Florence flask with ~500 mL of distilled water. Measure ~20 mL of 6 *M* NaOH into a graduated cylinder and pour the NaOH into the Florence flask. Stopper the flask, and carefully swirl to mix the solution.

2. Place the buret in a buret stand. Using a small funnel, half fill the buret with the NaOH solution from the Florence flask. Allow some solution to pass through the buret tip, invert the buret, and empty the remainder into the sink.

3. Close the stopcock, and fill the buret with NaOH solution from the Florence flask.

    Note: Carefully add NaOH solution to the funnel so as to not overfill the buret.

3. Label the 125-mL Erlenmeyer flasks #1, #2, and #3. Accurately weigh out ~1 g of KHP into each of the flasks. Add ~25 mL of distilled water to each flask, and heat as necessary to dissolve the KHP crystals.

4. Perform the titration as follows:
    * Drain some NaOH through the tip of the buret to clear any air bubbles.
    * Position Erlenmeyer flask #1 under the buret as shown in Figure 1.
    * Record the initial buret reading (± 0.05 mL).
    * Add a drop of phenolphthalein indicator to the flask.
    * Titrate the KHP sample to a permanent pink endpoint.
    * Record the final buret reading (± 0.05 mL).

5. Refill the buret with NaOH solution, record the initial buret reading, add a drop of phenolphthalein to flask #2, titrate the KHP sample and record the final buret reading.

6. Refill the buret with NaOH solution, record the initial buret reading, add a drop of phenolphthalein to flask #3, titrate the KHP sample and record the final buret reading.

7. Calculate the molarity of the NaOH solution for each trial. Record the average molarity of NaOH in the Data Table of Procedure B.

    Note: SAVE THE NaOH IN THE FLORENCE FLASK FOR PROCEDURE B.

B. Concentration of Acetic Acid in Vinegar

1. Obtain ~50 mL of vinegar solution in a dry 100-mL beaker. Record the unknown number in the Data Table.

2. Condition a pipet with unknown vinegar solution, and transfer a 10.0-mL sample into each 125-mL flasks. Add ~25 mL of distilled water into each flask.

    Note: It is not necessary to use dry flasks.

3. Fill the buret with NaOH solution, adjust the meniscus to zero, and record the initial buret reading as 0.00 mL. Add a drop of phenolphthalein to flask #1 and titrate the vinegar sample to a pink endpoint. Record the final buret reading.

4. Refill the buret with NaOH solution, and adjust the meniscus to 0.00 mL. Add a drop of phenolphthalein to flask #2, and titrate the vinegar sample.

   Note: By adjusting the meniscus to 0.00 mL, the endpoints for samples #2 and #3 should be at the same final buret reading as sample #1.

5. Refill the buret with NaOH solution and adjust the meniscus to 0.00 mL. Add a drop of phenolphthalein to flask #3, and titrate the vinegar sample.

6. Calculate the molarity of acetic acid, $HC_2H_3O_2$, in the unknown vinegar solution.

7. Convert the molarity of $HC_2H_3O_2$ (60.06 g/mol) to mass/mass percent concentration. Assume the density is 1.01 g/mL for the unknown vinegar solution.

   Note: WHEN THE TITRATIONS ARE COMPLETE, RINSE ALL GLASSWARE WITH DISTILLED WATER TO REMOVE ANY TRACES OF NaOH SOLUTION.

PRELABORATORY ASSIGNMENT*

1. In your own words define the following terms:

   conditioning

   endpoint

   indicator

   meniscus

   molar concentration (*M*)

   mass/mass percent concentration (m/m %)

   standardization

   titration

2. Observe and record the following buret readings.

(a)

(b)

---

*Answers at the end of the experiment.

3. How can you tell when the endpoint is near? What volume of NaOH is required to flip the indicator from colorless to pink at the endpoint ?

4. If KHP sample #1 requires 27.30 mL of NaOH solution to reach an endpoint, what volume should be required for samples #2 and #3?

5. If vinegar sample #1 requires 30.15 mL of NaOH solution to reach an endpoint, what volume should be required for samples #2 and #3?

6. Which of the following is a serious source of experimental error?

   (a) The sodium hydroxide is not mixed completely in the Florence flask.

   (b) The Florence flask is left unstoppered.

   (c) The buret is not conditioned.

   (d) The KHP samples are dissolved in 50 mL (not 25 mL) of distilled water.

   (e) Two drops (not one drop) of phenolphthalein indicator is used.

   (f) Bubbles are not cleared from the tip of the buret.

   (g) The Erlenmeyer flasks are not dried before weighing the KHP samples.

   (h) The Erlenmeyer flasks are not dried before pipetting the vinegar samples.

7. What safety precautions should be observed in this experiment?

NAME _____

DATE _____ SECTION _____

DATA TABLE

A. Preparation of Standard Sodium Hydroxide Solution

mass of Erlenmeyer flask + KHP	_____ g	_____ g	_____ g
mass of Erlenmeyer flask	_____ g	_____ g	_____ g
mass of KHP	_____ g	_____ g	_____ g
final buret reading	_____ mL	_____ mL	_____ mL
initial buret reading	_____ mL	_____ mL	_____ mL
volume of NaOH	_____ mL	_____ mL	_____ mL

Show the calculation of the molarity of NaOH for trial 1 (see Example Exercise 1).

Molarity of NaOH	_____ *M*	_____ *M*	_____ *M*
Average molarity of NaOH		_____ *M*	

B. Concentration of Acetic Acid in Vinegar   **UNKNOWN #** _____

Average molarity of NaOH (see Procedure A)   _____ *M*

volume of vinegar solution   _____ mL _____ mL _____ mL

final buret reading   _____ mL _____ mL _____ mL

initial buret reading   _____ mL _____ mL _____ mL

volume of NaOH   _____ mL _____ mL _____ mL

Show the calculation for the molarity of acetic acid for trial 1 (see Example Exercise 2).

Molarity of $HC_2H_3O_2$ _____ *M* _____ *M* _____ *M*

Show the calculation for the percent concentration of acetic acid for trial 1. (Assume the density of the vinegar solution is 1.01 g/mL.)

Mass/mass percent $HC_2H_3O_2$ _____ % _____ % _____ %

Average mass/mass percent $HC_2H_3O_2$ _____ %

Analysis of Vinegar

NAME _____

DATE _____   SECTION _____

POSTLABORATORY ASSIGNMENT

1. A sodium hydroxide solution is standardized using 0.502 g of solid oxalic acid, $H_2C_2O_4$. Find the molarity of the base if 30.50 mL are required for the titration to a phenolphthalein endpoint.

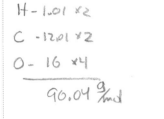

H - 1.01 ×2

C - 12.01 ×2

O - 16 ×4

_____

90.04 $\frac{g}{mol}$

$$H_2C_2O_4(s) + 2NaOH(aq) \rightarrow Na_2C_2O_4 (aq) + 2H_2O(l)$$

0.00580 mol acid = $\dfrac{0.0058 \text{ mol base}}{0.0305 \text{ L}}$ = _____ S L

_____

2. A 10.0-mL sample of household ammonia solution required 33.55 mL of 0.450 M HCl to reach neutralization. Calculate (a) the molar concentration of the ammonia and (b) the mass/mass percent concentration of ammonia (17.04 g/mol), given a solution density of 0.983 g/mL.

$$HCl (aq) + NH_3 (aq) \rightarrow NH_4Cl (aq)$$

$0.450 M = \dfrac{x \text{ moles}}{0.034 L}$

0.015 moles acid = $\dfrac{0.015 \text{ moles base}}{0.01 \text{ L}}$ = 1.5 M

(a) _____

(b) _____

3. If 22.50 mL of 0.100 M nitric acid is required to neutralize 25.0 mL of barium hydroxide solution, what is the molar concentration of the base?

$$2\,HNO_3 (aq) + Ba(OH)_2(aq) \rightarrow Ba(NO_3)_2 (aq) + 2H_2O(l)$$

$0.100 M = \dfrac{x \text{ moles}}{.0225 L}$

$\dfrac{.0225}{2}$ = $\dfrac{0.00113 \text{ moles}}{0.025 L}$ = 0.045

_____

4. A Rolaids tablet contains calcium carbonate, which neutralizes stomach acid. If 44.55 mL of 0.448 M hydrochloric acid is required to neutralize one tablet, how many milligrams of calcium carbonate are in a Rolaids tablet?

$$CaCO_3(s) + HCl\,(aq) \rightarrow CaCl_2\,(aq) + H_2O(l) + CO_2\,(g)$$

_____

5. (optional) A student carefully diluted 25.0 mL of 6 M NaOH solution in 475 mL of distilled water. Calculate the molarity of the diluted solution of base.

_____

Explain why this diluted NaOH solution cannot be used as a standard solution of base.

Answers to
Prelaboratory Assignment

ANALYSIS OF VINEGAR

1. See the Glossary.

2. (a) 0.50 mL   (b) 31.35 mL

3. As the endpoint is approached, flashes of pink color persist longer. At the endpoint, it only requires 1 drop of NaOH (~0.05 mL) to "flip" the indicator, and change the titrated solution from colorless to a permanent pink.

4. The volume of NaOH required to reach an endpoint will vary for each trial, depending on the mass of the KHP sample.

5. The volume of NaOH required to reach an endpoint should be about 30.15 mL for each trial because the amount of acetic acid is the same in each 10.0-mL vinegar sample.

6. (a), (b), (c), (f)

7. • Avoid contact with NaOH, especially near the eyes. In the event of contact, wash the area immediately with water and notify the Instructor.

   • Add NaOH carefully to avoid overfilling the buret NaOH by adding too much into the funnel.

   • Handle the pipet and buret carefully, as they are expensive and fragile pieces of glassware.